MW00618437

HOTELMAN

A MEMOIR

T. SCOTT BROWN

ARBUTUS PRESS
TRAVERSE CITY MI

Hotelman © 2014 T. Scott Brown

ISBN 978-1-933926-53-7
First Printing

Arbutus Press
Traverse City, Michigan
editor@arbutuspress.com
www.Arbutuspress.com
facebook.com/Arbutuspress
twitter@Arbutuspress

Printed in the United States of America

ACKNOWLEDGEMENTS

I want to thank Bea Sturgis, the former manager of my Seashell Beach Resort and now the general manager of my Kingsail Resort, for years of patience in reading, re-reading and listening to my story. "What did you really think when your dad said . . ." or "you didn't say that?" She made me dig deep.

And of course, I want to thank my family for not complaining about the countless nights I spent away from them in my offices writing.

DEDICATION

RAY BROWN

FOREWORD

This might be considered a "how to succeed in business" book because it does tell how I did it. It shows the personal cost and pain in persevering toward a dream, coupled with romance, friendship, and a glimpse into the privileged life of the wealthy in a summer resort town as I buck the establishment there. It's also a lesson in how to cook a damn good duck and how important that can be!

But foremost, mine is an old, old story of fathers and sons; how a boy becomes a man, wins his father's grudging approval, and ultimately finds for himself a home. Anyone with a strong, self-made father from "the greatest generation" or who wonders what it would have been like to have had one will relate to my tale.

Success doesn't come easy—that's why not everyone achieves it. It requires arduous hours of work, but also gained by being able to recognize opportunity and gamble with it—as well as trusting the advice of a friend. In reliving my life through this book, I've been amazed at how many critical junctures a unique friend stepped up to help me. No one does it alone. To succeed I accepted help from a widow in her nineties, a bohemian artist, and a failed flower shop owner turned clothing salesman.

My story is mostly set at the Colonial Inn in Harbor Springs, MI, a place that *Conde' Nast Traveler* described as "...your best chance of feeling welcome in a town where someone else's family has been summering since 1874."

By 1874, many wealthy manufacturing and industrial families of the Midwest had already chosen Harbor Springs, tucked away in the northwest corner of Michigan, as their spot to escape the summer heat. It's a leafy place of big homes, steep bluffs, and regattas with bright spinnakers plying dark blue waters, and its residents don't like change. Most of its long-time summer people have never wanted anyone else to come here. These families have tried for the most part to keep the town unchanged. There are no franchises or chain stores within miles, just cozy little shops and art galleries.

In 1894, twenty years after Harbor Springs had become known as a place to summer, a Civil War colonel built the Colonial Inn. Since he first stood on its pillared front porch and stretched his hand across the top of its wide front stairs to welcome guests, they've been made to feel at home.

My father, accompanied by his long-time chef and his second cook, took over the Colonial Inn almost seventy years later with probably the same desire; to make folks feel welcome. The guests said that when Dad shook their hand, they felt like they belonged. "I was only a secretary," a guest told me years after Dad died, "but your dad made me feel like I owned some big company."

Colonial Inn, with its manicured lawn, graceful walkways lined with red geraniums, and tall cedars looks pretty much the same as it did back in 1894, except that in the 1950's our east plaza, west plaza, and oval swimming pool were added. But these buildings have the same white clapboard siding, French doors, and green gables as the original inn.

I grew up in the hotel, watching doormen dressed as George Washington park Lincolns and big finned Cadillacs. (No foreign cars—this was Michigan.) In the 1970's I saw Mother host fashion shows with Lilly Pulitzer's yellow lion heads plastered on blue dresses and green sea serpents abounding on white pants accompanied by navy blazers.

I read our chef's recipes for Chicken Divan and Frozen Strawberries Romanoff in *Gourmet Magazine* and attended Mother's book signing party for her old friend Sonny Hemingway when she presented her new book *Ernie*, about her nephew—but without noticing that Mother had had cushions on the front porch redone in white chintz with yellow daises and green leaves for the affair.

The Colonial Inn is still a beautiful summer resort. But the glory days of the old guard—my father, mother, the chef Dario, and the rest— are now in the past. Yet they live on here as best as I can remember them.

Chapter 1

The Firm in Chicago

Quitting my job as a lawyer at a high-powered Chicago firm and going to work as a cook were the first unlikely steps on my winding road to success. Here's how it happened: with two business degrees from Michigan and a law degree from Notre Dame under my belt, I began my legal career in a large law firm occupying the tops floors of the American National Bank building in Chicago. But from the start I felt out of place sitting alone in my office cranking out briefs. The only time I saw anyone was when I went down the long hall to the firm's windowless library. Most of my time was spent sitting scrutinizing law books in the hope of finding the perfect case in support of a client whom I'd never meet. It was draining, to say the least.

I suppose that in time I might have become part of the firm's inner circle, met the clients, and been invited to their country clubs. But at the time all that seemed so far off. My decision to go to law school hadn't been thought out—my father wanted me to be a lawyer, and I wanted to please him. It was a thin thread upon which my life had been planned, and now it was being tested.

My life after work wasn't any more satisfying. I'd work till seven, ride the subway to Lincoln Park, grab a couple of drinks at Butch's, then walk the two blocks to my efficiency. I was too exhausted to even attempt dating. Once I asked a pretty girl sitting next to me on the train, "Could I look at your *Wall Street Journal*?" That was, alas, the closest I ever got to a girl.

I was surviving, existing from day to day, commuter ride to commuter ride, without any thought of making a change. My office was grim—my tiny desk might have made an intimate table for two. The wood paneling surrounding me was tired, but I did have a window that actually opened. The office was only temporary, I'd been told. They'd find an associate's cubicle for me soon. But nothing happened on that score.

One day in early December as I sat in my office hunched over a thick legal case book, a secretary entered and placed a manila envelope on my crowded desktop and left without a word. I glanced down and noticed that it was from the Board of Bar Examiners. I ripped it open and found I had passed the bar. I could now really call myself a lawyer. The years of hard work had finally paid off. I should have been elated, but I didn't give a damn. I crumpled the letter and threw it against the wall, where hung a print of George Washington and the colonial fathers signing the Declaration of Independence, looking to me like angry hotel guests who had been served a burnt chateaubriand.

The red light on my phone flashed. I picked up the receiver to hear the receptionist say, "It's your father."

"How goes it down there in the big city?" he said. "Wish I could trade places. Your mother and I are so proud. You're going to make a zillion dollars, maybe own the whole damn city of Chicago."

I cracked open the window behind my desk. I felt the cold air, heard the rush of traffic, and saw ant-sized people scurrying about on the street below. There was life out there—it was just that I was no longer a participant in it.

"Maybe so."

"Well, that's good. I know you will. As for us, your mother is tired of the hotel business. She wants to play more golf."

"Dad, what's going on?"

Just then the door to my office bolted open, and one of the senior partners entered. I hurriedly told Dad I'd call him back.

The partner stood in the door frame, not moving toward my desk.

"I heard you got a letter from the board of bar examiners. You passed, right?"

I looked up at him and nodded.

"There'll be a bonus," he said, and as an afterthought, "Oh, I'm taking my family to Michigan skiing. What's that little town you're from?"

"Harbor Springs, sir."

"Yeah, that's it. We're going to Boyne. They'll have the skis outside our door the next morning and Austrians teaching our kids. Hell, they'll be going down double diamonds at the end of the week."

"Yes, I took lessons from the Austrians in high school," I said.

What I didn't say was that I paid for them with favors, like cozy window tables in the dining room, the right bottle of Bordeaux, and knowing which of their girlfriends liked extra anchovies on her Caesar salad.

"Wasn't that ski resort the place your old man tried to develop?

I nodded, wishing that I had never tried to build up my family during my job interview.

"Too bad he didn't have the guts to go through with it. Think where you'd be. Anyway, you passed the bar. Take tomorrow off. In a couple of years you'll be able to take a ski week."

My heart sank as I pictured myself flying down the slopes with a little blonde—in a couple of years.

"By the way, that was a terrific job you did last week on the pleadings for the Russell case; stroke of brilliance citing those off-point cases. Those meatheads on the other side wasted two whole days arguing relevancy with the judge. I love it when plaintiffs' lawyers have a lot of non-billable time. Just don't do it again with that judge; he's on to you."

"Yeah, we took it to them," I said with false bravado, covering the fact that the "off-point cases" were nothing more than a mistake on my part, not brilliant strategy.

"Well, hang in there. My secretary will have a new list of topics to research after your day off. Get some rest."

He left with the same abruptness with which he had entered. I sat there looking at the back of the door thinking that I could do more skiing by mid-morning than that fat ass could do in a day. And he didn't have any right to cut my Dad down. Dad didn't have the power of a Chicago senior partner, but he knew how to make things happen. Whenever Michigan played for the Big Ten championship, he knew who to call to get tickets: the coach's barber, who vacationed at our hotel. "It's not what you know," Dad would say, "it's who you know." I was worrying what Dad was going to tell me when he called. He had blind-sided me when he'd called the previous week. There'd been the same few minutes of chit-chat. Then he'd said that Dario had died.

It had taken a moment for the news to settle it. Dead? Dario couldn't have been dead. He was in Florida, playing golf or fishing. It wasn't possible. After the call I had rushed out of the office to the nearest bar, leaving stacks of unfinished work.

Dario, a Filipino, was Dad's best friend and chef at the hotel since Dad had purchased it. Over the years I had spent many afternoons in the kitchen with him, learning his techniques for roasting ducks, making a good Béarnaise sauce, and getting rack of lamb done just right. He was the heart and soul of the Colonial Inn. And now he was dead.

I recalled his last words to me, as I drove him to the Pellston Airport just a month earlier, when the hotel closed for the season. "I know for now you going to be lawyer, but cooking still in your future. I see it. Put plenty of booze on duck—cook hell out of it. Use Grand Marnier, no cheap stuff like your Dad. You come to hotel and see me next summer. I won't always be here. I've made you chef. One day you own hotel." An unlikely prophecy, I thought at the time, what with my legal career laid out for me.

Later that afternoon, I was finally able to call Dad back, with some trepidation, and ask what was on his mind. He got right to the point. "A real estate developer is going to give me a bundle for the hotel. He's going to tear it down and build condos."

"What? Sell the hotel? How can you? It's been our life."

"Yeah, but we'll still have the memories, and I won't have any stress."

For some reason I pictured Mother walking me up the front stairs to the hotel verandah on my eighth birthday. Dad stood at the top wearing his red sports coat. I was so proud. We were the Browns of the Colonial Inn. We couldn't be anything else. During all the time that I had planned a legal career, I always pictured Mother and Dad still back at the hotel. I never thought otherwise. The hotel, I thought, would always be there.

"You're going to let someone tear the place down?"

I imagined a wrecking ball swinging into the hotel.

"When did you become so sensitive?"

"Can we talk? Don't sign anything! I need time."

"Time for what?" yelled Dad. "It's my decision. You're just being informed." Then he seemed to cool. "Well, it'll take a few days for the lawyers to draw up the papers."

"A few days, thanks."

"But it won't make any difference. The hotel is going to be sold." With that he hung up.

I sat there in my office chair as if glued to it, without the strength or will to move. I gazed up at the ceiling. As long as Dad still owned the hotel, I could kid myself into believing that my life in Chicago wasn't permanent. I had been able to survive by imagining that my legal work was like another year of graduate school that would come to an end in the spring.

But soon I started to work past my own feelings of disbelief and sadness and began to focus on why he wanted to sell. Maybe I would find a clue, something that might help me convince him not to sell.

I guessed that he didn't want to sell just so he could play more golf with Mother. The hotel had been his life. That couldn't be replaced with golf. Perhaps Dad's love for the hotel had died with Dario, who was as much a part of the hotel as the cedar posts that held it up. Maybe he didn't think he could go on without Dario. To Dad, it was his old-timers who had been important. I had to convince him that as long as the hotel survived, there would be new people, new relationships. It was the place itself that mattered.

On the way home that evening I stopped off at a neighborhood bar, intending to have just one drink to loosen up. However, after several hours of drinking, I was still there. I tried to score a girl, but failed, or just failed being interested. It didn't matter, and I stumbled the few blocks home to my efficiency.

When I got there I looked out the window from my one-room apartment that had barely enough room for a bed and a TV. Across the street was a big square building just like mine, and in it lived people in little square boxes just like me. My neighbors and I were stacked one on top of each other like the manila boxes in which Dad stored the hotel records.

Lying gin-soaked on my couch, I saw that I was never going to be the high-powered corporate attorney that my parents envisioned; nor did I want to be.

But I understood why Dad wanted me to succeed in the larger world. Although we owned the only hotel in Harbor Springs, and a highly successful one, at that we were second-class citizens there and always would be. I guess Dad wanted something better than that for me. But for me, despite whatever dubious social status I might have among the old summer families of Harbor Springs, the hotel was precious to me. To understand my dilemma then, you have to know Harbor Springs.

Its only two summer associations, seasonal home to rich out-of-towners, are Wequetonsing (pronounce it Wee-quee-ton-sing or they'll know you don't belong) and Harbor Point (simply called "the Point"). Wequetonsing, where Colonial Inn lies, faces about a mile of water frontage with numerous "cottages" behind—the cottages commonly three-story mansions with twenty rooms and servants. The cottages are all numbered and kept respectfully to only a few digits. If you have a long address, with say four digits, which some of the newer homes a few miles away have, then you're new to the area and not old money. If you are riding a bike or walking through their grounds, someone might say, "Are you from the town?" implying that they don't know you and therefore assume you're probably a service person.

Harbor Point, a one-mile-long peninsula, juts out into Lake Michigan on the other side of town, giving Harbor Springs a wonderfully protected natural harbor. The Point doesn't allow automobiles from July 4th to Labor Day. Everyone must commute to the town by their own speedboat or bike, or ride one of the association's yellow carriages with red and white striped canvas top. The only narrow entrance to the Point is gated and simply no one gets out there who doesn't belong.

The prevailing attitude of the moneyed folks at both summer associations was once summed up for me by one of their children: "Everyone says that your father owns that hotel only to make money," implying that we should be content just to service the resort community rather than worrying about filthy profits.

But if you're one of the summer people, you perhaps don't have to worry about such distasteful pecuniary matters. If great-grandfather was really something, he came north on the weekends in July and August on his private train car, which was left on a siding in back of the cottage. And if your trust was properly set up, there's enough money to carry you to the end of your days.

When not "summering" at Harbor Springs, you may dabble in heirloom tomatoes in Palm Beach or as a stockbroker in Gross Pointe with only a few preferred clients (probably your own trust and the trusts of a few close friends.) Or you might work for a nonprofit corporation—quite respectable. (It's likely that your family funded the nonprofit, which means they have to give you a job.) Or you might not work at all, simply saying that you do investments or real estate, though the latter is sometimes frowned upon.

I once overheard one of the resorters, when asked what he did, reply in an irritated manner, "Nothing, absolutely nothing. I don't HAVE TO DO ANYTHING."

But if you don't have such overbearing arrogance, and have reached a certain age, you can simply say that you are retired, though without implying from what. That, too, is quite acceptable.

But even if the money has run out or you've squandered it in some acceptable way and are now forced to work at a regular job, that's okay. You are still accepted socially because it's your birth connection to the summer association, and the fact that you grew up among these folks that make you who you are, not the vagaries of money's ebb and flow.

If you're fortunate enough to be from an old family, until the 1980's, you carried charge accounts at the local stores, even the ice cream parlor and gas station, where your offspring and servants charged freely. Charges grew all summer, then often weren't settled up until the following June, leaving the local proprietors to carry the millionaires' incidentals for the winter.

However, even today, the cottage where you summer, most likely a rambling, multi-fireplaced, century-old, clapboard property on the shores of Lake Michigan, may have been in the family for generations, with the estate divided up so many times that the great-grandchildren of the original owner may each have only a week's use of the cottage. The head of the water department in Harbor Springs once told me that it wasn't uncommon to have had a number of the water meters in Wequetonsing read three and even four times in a month. These supposedly wealthy grandchildren were concerned about not paying any of their brothers' or cousins' water usage.

The grandmother may have been pushed aside by a divorce or disinterest in her. She's purchased a cheaper home not on the water or even in town, but still wants to properly socialize on the porch of the cottage. In such instances "porch rights" are granted to Grandmother or Aunt Hortense to come sit for cocktails or even, on a limited basis, to host her own cocktail party there.

But if you're from new money people, such as my family, and without social ties, then you're not considered socially acceptable. You're simply not from an "old family." If that be the case, you'll never become a member of the nearby golf club, which, as I've learned through personal experience, never embarrasses anyone by rejecting their application outright, but rather places them on "permanent hold."

However, even if you're not one of them, sometimes you're permitted to rub elbows with the old families. For example, once a week during "the season" the Wequetonsing association hosts a "hot dog cookout" on the grounds of their "casino," an old recreation hall where the children are entertained in organized and supervised summer programs. Some folks from outside the association are able to attend if they have children in the summer program. (Outside children are allowed in to help reduce the costs, as these folks often aren't as wealthy as they may appear.)

But, as I embarrassingly learned, "hot dog night" has nothing to do with hot dogs. I brought hot dogs for the common grill, not knowing that "everyone" brings filet mignons or lobster tails to cook. Further, no one would talk to me or even look at me; I was the invisible man. When I saw one of my former hotel guests, who now owned a small house in town and also had kids in the summer program, I asked her to join me at a small table I found in back. She declined with darting eyes, saying it had taken years for her to be accepted and now she had to eat with her people or there would be trouble.

But despite all its snobbery, I loved Harbor Springs—the lake, the wooded hills, and the sense of freedom it always presented to me. It was home, the place where I found security and strength. That night in Chicago as I contemplated Dad's decision to sell the hotel, the thought of losing it forever chilled me to my bones.

It was now eleven o'clock, but Dad would still be up having a drink. I grabbed the phone.

When he answered, I blurted, "Dad, I don't want you to sell! I passed the bar exam today, but you know what? It doesn't matter. I hate being a lawyer. I want to come home and run the hotel."

There, I had said it. My stomach was in knots as I awaited his reply.

Finally he bellowed. "You've got to be kidding! I've already kept the hotel five years longer than I planned just because of you, waiting till you got settled. I never made any real money running the hotel. That was supposed to come when I sold. I waited my whole life for this; big money safely in the bank and no worries. Do you realize what you're asking?"

"Yes," I said, with no thought I'd asked him to put the rest of his life on hold. "You don't really want to sell."

"You're not cutting it in the big law firm, is that it? You want to come back here and let me take care of everything while you chase the college girls."

That hurt. I bit my tongue instead of angrily telling him to just go ahead and sell if he wanted.

I was desperate. Our conversation had become adversarial, and somehow I had to change the tone. If I could get Dad to start reminiscing, then maybe I could get him to see that the hotel itself was bigger than Dario, and that he could go on without him. Dad had lost other close employees and gone on. He could do it again

"Dad, remember when you met Dario at the race track in Miami? You had blown a lot of cash and the little Filipino with a feather sticking out of his straw hat next to you had won big."

"That was because he knew all the jockeys. They all came to the hotel where he was the chef."

I led him on, "Was that when you decided to offer him the chef's job at the hotel?"

"Nah, I was more interested in getting to know the jockeys. I didn't offer him the job for a few more weeks."

We went on talking about how he and Dario had both loved to gamble for the thrill of it, not just for the money. He said it was like overselling hotel rooms or double-booking a table at the restaurant, then having things work out in the end.

Dad began talking about Benny, our long-time second cook, and his knack for gossip. The guests actually relished being let in on his talk, and felt special because of it. When they returned each summer, they could hardly wait to have him carve them prime rib at their table and get the scoop on who was having sex with whom and who wasn't.

"It's been five years since Benny died. I wondered how we could go without him, but we did."

I heard him breathing over the line. Finally, in softened voice, he said, "I've been thinking about all that; Benny and now Dario. What I wouldn't give to have them back."

"Dad, admit it, you're not ready to quit. You love the hotel. Dario and Benny are gone, but that doesn't mean that the hotel has to be sold. We went on without Benny and we can go on without Dario. I know Dario did a lot for you, but we'll find a new chef, and I'll run the hotel. You can begin to take it easier. Hell, I'm ready. And my business and legal training will come in handy."

He didn't say a thing, so I went on. "It hit me today how much the place means to me. I don't want to lose it."

I imagined the turmoil in his mind. He'd made his decision, and now I had complicated it. Would he have another chance to sell if things didn't work out? I waited while he thought. At last he said, "All right. You can come home and help me with the hotel. I'll put the deal on hold, at least for another summer. You know that summer is what I care about. But, if you're that anxious to get out of Chicago, I'll have the west building opened up for the winter so you'll have something to do."

Then before I could thank him or get in a word, Dad went on, "I can't make any promises. Is that good enough? Should I have the west plaza opened?"

"I'll be home in a week."

When we hung up, I collapsed onto the sofa.

I was relieved, not elated. I wasn't sure how much confidence Dad had in me, nor what "help me with the hotel" meant. Did he trust me to run the hotel? We'd had some ferocious arguments in the past, and I feared that, working together, we would again.

Dad had agreed to opening the hotel's west building of fourteen rooms for the winter. I'd receive no pay, but if there were any profits, and Dad doubted that there would be, I could keep them. Previously Dad had tried unsuccessfully to keep the entire hotel open in the winter. But I'd have a low-risk operation with only one building and virtually no overhead, so I'd have a chance of making some money. Maybe it wouldn't be very profitable, but at least I wouldn't have to do anymore legal research.

Chapter 2

Dr. Zhivago had nothing on this

A red sun was vanishing into the western ice on Little Traverse Bay when I pulled up in front of the hotel one week later. The ice on the northern Great Lakes doesn't just happen at once. Thin sheets of ice that can stretch for miles form on cold nights in December, then the next day the wind breaks them up. But the ice doesn't go away. The pieces wash back and forth, sticking to each other, gradually growing into mini-icebergs that get pushed up onto the shore. The next night the top half inch of the lake freezes again, and the day after the north wind does its job by making more icebergs and joining them to those already made. This goes on for weeks, like a little kid putting Legos together, and gradually the ice resembles frozen waves stretching out from the shore. It looks much like the waves of a rough summer's day somehow instantly froze.

I slowly got out of my Mustang. The cold air hit me as I looked up at the pine trees surrounding the hotel. They seemed like black giants, with their snow-laden boughs waiting for the dark. A feeling of loneliness came over me. Was I doing the right thing? I closed the door to the car and stared up at the white columns of the dark hundred-year-old hotel. It looked like the frozen ice palace of *Dr. Zhivago*.

My boots crunched on the hard-packed ice as I climbed over a four-foot snow bank that had been pushed up in front of the hotel from weeks of plowing. But on the other side of the mound, with each successive step,

I sunk several feet in the unpacked snow under the now-bare frame of the entrance canopy. Finally, after some struggling, I reached the front steps and began climbing.

At the top I crossed the green-carpeted front porch and stood at the grand entrance. After fumbling in my pocket for the key, I opened the door with a creak, shattering the silence.

Somehow the dark, unheated hotel felt even colder than the unprotected outside. The last rays of the day's sun were bending their way through the old wavy glass of the lobby windows. I walked slowly across the big white ceramic tiled lobby floor, each step echoing against the high walls. Memories lay everywhere. Except for sheets hanging over the drapes and the plastic over the furniture, everything looked as it had on closing day—pristine.

I needed one of Dad's martins. Why not? The Tanqueray would be at the bar right around the corner, and I deserved one. It had been a long trip, and the porch looked perfect for a cocktail party of one.

I walked through the dark lobby to the cocktail lounge, went behind the bar, and grabbed a glass. As I opened the hidden door to the liquor storeroom, I smiled, remembering that Dad had fashioned this door to blend into the woodwork behind the bar, to make it less enticing for the college help. It didn't work. They all knew where the door was. Inevitably a bartender would forget to lock it or an enterprising busboy would pick it, and there'd be a party in the waitress dorm.

I fumbled in the growing darkness until I was able to pull down the bottles of gin and vermouth from the old wooden shelves and make a "martin" as Dad called it, minus the olives and lemon twist. The gin, thrillingly cold, bit my tongue; perfection, just the way that Dad liked it. He said that gin is best when it comes right out of the freezer and nips at the roof of your mouth. Tonight no freezer was needed.

I took my drink, went back through the lobby, and pulled one of the wicker chairs out onto the porch. In the process gin sloshed over the rim of my cocktail, causing my fingers to become frozen to the side of the glass and covering the black outline of the colonial bell crier. It was cold.

Nonetheless, I sat and stared down the street toward the bay where the sun was beginning to vanish. A confusing rush of relief, fear, and nostalgia rose in me. I felt relieved to be home, scared to death that I might be screwing up my life, and melancholy, thinking about the hotel without Dario and Benny. Looking back, I marvel at my composure; relaxing and even sipping a martin, while my future hung in the unknown.

How could I have been drinking a martin? I should have been drinking *many* martins.

Twenty minutes later, the sun was about to slip over the horizon on the cloudless night. I waited and there it was; the green flash that comes up out of nowhere when the sun vanishes. It's only possible on perfectly clear evenings, usually in the dead of winter, but sometimes in the summer when there's no haze. Although rarely seen in the summer, Dad never failed to mention it at his cocktail parties. It gave the guests something unusual to ponder and made them think that their innkeeper was a knowledgeable man.

I wanted to stay on the icy porch, linger at my own party, tell stories, exaggerate them, and entertain myself—and drink another martin perhaps. My stories would be fascinating. I could make them up, as Dad did during his nightly cocktail parties. With no one to question my tales, I could practice, but I knew I'd never be as good as Dad. Bending the truth was his special realm.

I leaned back in my chair like Dad used to, took a final sip of my martin, and pictured him wearing his geranium-red sport coat on a warm July night. He always wore that coat when he was holding court on this porch. It contrasted with the navy sport coats worn by the guests and stood out from the bright Lilly Pulitzer flower-pattern dresses.

"These guests have a fancier education and a lot more money than me, but goddamn it, it's my hotel," Dad said on more than one occasion.

He didn't need the sport coat to attract attention. His six-foot-two-inch frame and heavily caffeinated personality engulfed the porch, leaving little room for any other would-be extroverts. He'd talk about his two years of second-string football at the University of Miami as if he'd played with the best. At one of Dad's porch parties I once heard him say, "We all played at the same time," to Wisconsin's Elroy "Crazy Legs" Hirsch and Michigan's Forest Evasheyski. There was no doubt in my mind that Dad was hoping that the other guests listening would picture him perhaps tackling these legendary All-American running backs.

But football wasn't everything; just ninety percent of the conversation. Once he turned to a white-haired lady sitting alone in the corner of the porch, who looked like she'd expended a lot of effort just getting there. "I've heard that you were a great golfer."

The lady answered that when she was young she had won her club championship in Kankakee. "That must have really been a match. Tell us about it. Listen up, everyone. We've got a story here."

The lady went on with the not-too-interesting details of her long-ago golf match. After a few minutes of talking, smiling, and watching all the other guests focus on her, she started losing steam. Heads were beginning to turn away just when Dad leaned over her and interrupted. "So you won the championship. I've seen a lot of football games go down to the wire like that. Reminds me of when I was at Miami . . ."

With the sun gone, the cold was now unbearable. My solitary cocktail party would have to continue in my room. My life, that winter anyway, wouldn't be catering to wealthy patrons in the dining room, lounge, and porch of the main inn. No, I'd be running a fourteen-unit motel, open to skiers in blue jeans. But money is money, all green, and I desperately needed it.

I left the porch, groping my way through the darkness back to the liquor storeroom, and grabbed the Tanqueray and vermouth. Locking up the hotel, I stomped through the snow past tall cedars and around our pool toward our west building. From the twilight remaining I could see that the pool was iced over, which gave me a deep chill. It was hard to think that months earlier I had been swimming after a red-haired college waitress in that now-frozen pool. (A lot of folks think hotel pools are drained in the winter, but they're left full. The weight of the water keeps them from lifting out of the ground during the spring thaws.)

Across the grounds, still grasping my bottles, I pushed the French doors open to my suite in our west building. The heat sizzled from the radiator in the corner, making the room warm and toasty. I flicked a match and lit the fire that had already been prepared in the fireplace. I mixed another martin and sank into a blue-and-white checkered Queen Anne's chair. Suddenly I felt it; loneliness.

There would be no office to go to tomorrow with folks shuffling about, just more of being alone at the closed hotel. There wouldn't be any guests until Christmas, and that was two weeks away. I'd have to be here in this room day and night answering the phone or there wouldn't be any guests. I saw that I needed a friend, someone to talk to.

How about a dog? I thought. That'd be a good companion, wouldn't it? We'd had a Saint Bernard when I was a boy; he was my buddy, sleeping right by my bed.

I remembered a lilac-scented night in June long ago when I was eight. I sat taking in the stillness on our porch watching the fireflies' behinds glow as Dad got drunk. After his fourth martini, he looked over at me. "When I was a boy, I wanted a dog, but we couldn't afford it. Let's get one now—how about a big one like a Saint Bernard?"

He got up, went into the kitchen, and started making phone calls, as if ordering a Saint Bernard at eleven o'clock at night was perfectly normal. When he finally reached a kennel, I could tell the call wasn't warmly received from the way he held the receiver back from his ear. But he went on. "Yeah, I know you have dogs waiting to be shipped to Europe, but I NEED ONE NOW." Some minutes later he set the phone down, went back to his lounge chair, lit a cigarette, and announced, "Your puppy will arrive on the six a.m. flight."

When we picked up Teddy Bear, as I named him, a note pinned to his cage said that he was already housebroken and could shake, sit, and lie down. I could tell from the stiff grin on Dad's face that, now sober, he realized that this dog wasn't going to be cheap. He'd given the kennel his credit card number without asking the cost, which turned out to be a thousand dollars, one sixth the cost of a new Cadillac at that time.

Mother, who hadn't been consulted, wasn't expecting a dog and certainly hadn't planned on an enormous animal, was stunned. But she went along; it was just part of living with Dad.

I savored my third martini as the fire burnt low and decided now was the time to order another Saint Bernard. Hell, it was only ten o'clock at night, early for ordering a dog by Dad's standards. After a call to information, I reached the Von Schwartz Kennels, which had sent us Teddy Bear twenty years earlier.

When a lady with a scratchy voice answered the phone, I announced, "This is Tim Brown of the Colonial Inn."

"Oh my God, I remember you. I worried about that dog. . . But you sounded alright, so I sent him anyway. But I called the airport to make sure that somebody picked him. I didn't want one of puppies sitting in a fright hanger unwanted. The circumstances were so strange."

"That was my father. We had Teddy for ten years, a wonderful dog."

"Were you the little boy whom he said it was an emergency to get the dog for? Your Dad must have really loved you."

"Yeah, I answered, remembering that Dad had always been a mixture of love and toughness. "I want another dog."

"How many cocktails have you had?"

Ignoring her question, I shot back, "I loved that dog. We had him ten years, though he probably would have lived longer if the cook hadn't put bacon grease on his food every morning—a benefit of living at the hotel. Saint Bernards don't live much past ten anyway, do they?"

"The grease didn't help."

"I'm spending the winter in a closed hotel, no wife, no girlfriend, and it's lonely as hell. I need a dog!"

"You want another pick of the litter?"

I hadn't consumed so many martins that I'd forgotten about my money straits. "How much is this going to cost? I just quit my job and don't have a lot of money."

I heard labored breathing over the phone while she was probably assessing how much I could pay, then slowly she answered, "I've got just the dog, a three-month-old puppy, just returned by its owner. These big dogs aren't for everyone. But he's top of the line and trained. You can have him for four hundred. I'll throw in shipping. Maybe I can get him on the morning flight."

Seven hours later with the night still black, I headed to the airport. I'd call him Teddy Bear as well, I decided. Why not? It was a good name for another martin-ordered dog.

During the next two weeks the grayness of winter closed in on me. I sat by the fire, watched my puppy sleep, and made pleading phone calls to the Chamber of Commerce, the ski resorts, and anyone else I could think of who might send me business. The hotel had only been open for two winters in the previous ten years, so there was no established winter clientele. No one even thought of the Colonial Inn as a place to stay in the winter.

Here I was in the Midwest's finest ski area, yet I couldn't go skiing. I had to sit in my makeshift office and wait for the phone to ring. I escaped my boredom through adventure novels and daydreaming about what a fine job I was going to do for Dad when spring came. But my tenacity and discipline ultimately paid off. Slowly, with just one or two reservations a day, it worked. I had a full house for the holidays.

With the holidays came my first Christmas alone, but I was too busy to think much about it. My fourteen-room operation turned out to be much harder than I had expected. With only one housekeeper I was as busy as I had been on any July night as maitre d', except that instead of making Caesar salads, carving chateaubriands, and flambéing desserts, I was plunging toilets, carrying dirty linen, and shoveling snow. But I was actually having a great time. I liked having the guests around. Each evening I hosted a cocktail party for my guests by my fire. I'd sit with them comparing skiing stories. Depending on how much we drank, Scarface ski run at Nub's Nob or Challenger at Boyne would be as harrowing as any ski run out west.

When New Years ended and the guests checked out, the reality of winter set in. The ski business in northern Michigan really exists only on the weekends, when everyone comes north from Chicago, Detroit, and northern Ohio. The few folks who do come midweek usually end up staying right at the slopes or renting a condo, so there isn't much business for the other hotels. That was probably why Dad had found being open in the winter unprofitable. But I had a staff of only one housekeeper, who was happy to have a lot of time off, so I decided to turn the heat down, trust my reservations to an answering machine, and close Sunday to Friday. Since I wouldn't be making any money then, I'd just go skiing. It was a great idea; I'd keep the profits from the weekends and cut the losses from the week, except that I had a lot of lonely nights without guests.

On a blustery Tuesday morning in early January, alone in my suite in the west building, I woke up, opened the French doors leading to my porch, and let Teddy out. The loose snow that had been ringing the door panes blew in my face with a blast of arctic wind. Brrr! Having been snuggled in my warm bed, I felt like I'd just entered the hotel's walk-in freezer on a hot day. After barely a couple of minutes, I heard Teddy's big paws knocking at the door to come in. It was too cold out there even for a Saint Bernard. I threw a couple of extra logs on the fire and was glad that I had nowhere to go. I'd spend the whole day by the fire reading. Some guests had left a Harlequin romance book, not something that I'd normally read, but since I was alone in a snowstorm, it'd do.

The phone rang. It was a woman from Naples, Florida who wanted to book for the month of July. "I've heard that Harbor Springs is an old fashioned place. There aren't many places left like that and I'd like to spend time there. I hate chain hotels, too. They're all the same. When you're in 'em, it's like being in a showroom of a department store—too polished. I want to stay in a place with character," she said in direct tone.

I laughed and the conversation went on for a bit. I felt that I was establishing a relationship with her, something I thought Dad would want me to do. She sounded like she belonged at our hotel, so I told her that I'd call her back with some room selections and rates. Then I called Dad.

"I'll handle it," he said and went on talking for some time about how difficult it was to take reservations, implying that he didn't think that I was up to the task. "You've got to massage the prospective guests before closing the deal," he repeated several times.

I listened, thinking that I'd been handling the reservations for the winter and it hadn't been that hard. I wanted to take that reservation and show Dad that I could do it. "I'll call her back. Just tell me what kind of deal you give long-term stays and which efficiencies are open."

"It's not that simple. I got to talk to her, see what she'll pay. You're not ready for this."

I hung up reluctantly. The receiver made a hollow thud as it hit the phone. I now realized that he didn't trust me with reservations—the life blood of the hotel as he proclaimed. I began to worry about the coming summer. What exactly would I be doing? What had I been thinking? I couldn't see Dad stepping aside and letting me run the hotel.

I looked up toward the French doors in my suite. Although it seemed like hours, it had only been a few minutes since I had opened them for Teddy to come in, shaking off the snow. But their panes were again completely dusted with the white stuff, making it impossible to see out. I felt the same way about trying to look at my future. I couldn't see it. If Dad had been willing to retire by selling the hotel, then why couldn't he step aside and let me run it? I'd worked there since childhood, doing every conceivable job. I thought that I was ready.

I figured that the profits from running the hotel would have been just as much as the interest on the proceeds of a sale. But thinking back, I can see that interest from bank CD's would have been a sure thing, whereas the hypothetical profits from a young kid running the hotel were far from certain. If he'd sold, he would have had money and wouldn't have to worry. But with me running the hotel, he'd have to worry. Having grown up in the Great Depression, Dad would often say, "Hell, I don't care what they say, it could happen again. Everybody thought railroad jobs were safe, but my dad got laid off. In the end all you really got is yourself."

I pictured Dad, white-haired and tanned, in his navy bathing suit, sitting now on his Florida balcony overlooking the Atlantic answering his phone. He'd set down his cup of black coffee next to his ash tray full of Camel butts, pick up the phone, and say, "Of course, Mrs. Wood. If you're from Naples, I don't need a deposit. I've got a ground floor suite overlooking the pool for you right next to Suttons from Naples."

Then, after he'd talked her into staying an extra couple of weeks, he'd set the phone down like it was a poker hand he'd just won with. He was in complete control, a person who savored his business, a person who would rather sell a customer than do most anything else.

I wondered if I was ready to fill his shoes.

Chapter 3

The only guy who knew where the pipes were

When the last snowstorm of April iced the trees, it seemed that winter was never going to end. But two weeks after I shoveled the steps to the west plaza for the last time, the thermometer hit seventy degrees. Within the space of another week, I watched the barren woods come alive with white trilliums.

Soon our former groundskeeper would be arriving to turn the water on for the summer in the rest of hotel. I couldn't be sure exactly when he was coming, because even when he was actively working for us, his hours were a mystery known only to himself. But somehow even between bouts of heavy drinking his work got done efficiently, leaving the grounds pristine, so John remained in Dad's good graces. Even in the spring of 1980, having been retired for years, John was still draining the hotel in the fall and putting the water back on in the spring because Dad didn't trust anyone else to do it. This was probably because John was the only one who knew where all the pipes were, and he'd never bothered to show anyone else—perfect job security. I reasoned that was why Dad never said anything about his drinking.

Back in the 1950's the weathermen on our two TV channels seemed to be wrong most of the time. They erred on the side of rain, causing guests to check out early, which wasn't a good thing for Dad's mortgage. So he found a more optimistic weather predictor—John. A full-blooded Odawa Indian, he got pretty good at predicting the weather, at least by

Dad's standards, since he erred on the side of sunshine. Whenever a guest questioned John's forecasting, Dad would say, "His people have been here since the beginning of time. He ought to know."

For a number of years John had also been in charge of hiring the bellboys at the hotel. In a normal hotel with clearly defined channels of command, a grounds man would never have been in charge of the bellmen, but at the Colonial Inn where there was no real sense of organization, only Dad's capricious methods, this seemed quite natural.

Since John was from Harbor Springs, Dad figured that he'd be better suited at picking out the local boys for the job. John would teach them how to grunt and groan just the right amount when they wrestled the guests' big suitcases up to their rooms. This he'd found greatly increased the boys' tips, which were important to John because he demanded a cut of them. John had discovered early on that a number of the wealthy hotel guests and resorters having their cars parked while coming in for dinner thought the privilege of serving them counted for most of the tip. "A few beads of sweat and a slight cough will correct that misrepresentation," John would instruct the wide-eyed boys.

Just to keep the boys on their best tip-generating behavior and to see that they weren't cheating him on his cut of the tips, John would try to be sober one night a week. He would don the George Washington costume, the outfit worn by the hotel's official parking attendant, and regulate the bellboys. To Dad's great satisfaction, this kept them on their toes because no one, including John, could ever be sure what night he was going to be sober enough to come in. Since Dad didn't pay John anything extra for this, and Dad was getting essentially a free head bellman out of his groundskeeper, Dad must have considered this a great deal, all drinking aside.

And John had another important duty. In the off-season before leaving for Florida, Mom and Dad had tried to fashion a life of social elegance where someone else assumed the mundane task of driving their child around the bay to school. This allowed them to both sleep off the effects of their previous evening and prepare for their afternoon golf games. In September and October when the hotel was closed, John was the only one around, so the task fell to him.

Now, on an exceptionally warm morning in late April, John showed up with pipe wrenches bulging from his pockets and a cigarette hanging from the corner of his mouth. Except for his now-white hair, he looked just like he had in the days he was driving me to elementary school.

As I headed across the hotel grounds behind John, who wasn't saying a word, I felt an empty feeling. The lake was still, not a leaf appeared on any tree and not a single bird sang. All I could hear was the clinking of his pipe wrenches as he ambled along. The bareness of early spring made the vastness of the hotel grounds quite apparent. The Colonial Inn had been built at a time when labor was cheap, so its buildings were spread out over a lot of land, which required meticulous care. Further, the cost of maintenance and servicing of the rooms were far in excess of that of similar sized modern hotels contained in one building and situated on a smaller, more appropriate piece of land.

At that time, the rooms at the Colonial Inn were called studios, a term that no one has heard of today. This meant that the rooms contained two twin beds in an L shape in the corner with pillow bolsters giving the appearance of two couches. There was a coffee table between beds so the guests could entertain in their hotel room as if it was an apartment. Even in the late seventies this had become an outmoded design with few people understanding or appreciating it, making it difficult to explain to potential guests.

This room configuration was uniquely beautiful, but created a nightmare for the housekeepers tucking the sheets in and fitting the custom four cornered bed spreads. These kinds of beds required nightly turn down service because none of the guests, even the old timers, could figure out how they worked.

The rooms also had real wood burning fireplaces, which was a great selling feature, but expensive to maintain. In years past John had found some local boy willing to clean out the fireplaces and rekindle them with new wood every morning for little money, but that had all passed. I sensed that the hotel was moving into a time with economics that Dad didn't fully understand. Providing great food and service or being known as a gracious innkeeper simply wasn't going to be enough. I knew that changes had to be coming and vowed to discuss them with Dad when he returned.

As I was attempting to add up the extra costs that Colonial Inn was incurring, John stopped in front of the main inn and stared right at it without moving a muscle. His forehead appeared to be wrinkled in thought. "I'd like to teach you the plumbing," he offered.

I hadn't expected that. I'd only planned on walking over to the main inn, visiting for a bit, then leaving. I'd wanted to get back to my suite, light a fire, plop myself down in front of it, and finish the book I had left. I hesitated, thinking about what John had said. Since he was a man of few words, it took a while to realize that he was offering more than a plumbing lesson. But still I wasn't looking forward to a day of hard manual labor, so I only gave a half hearted turn and nodded.

John's leathery face creased a smile, and we went up the front steps together, the beginning of a long day. His stale whiskey breath was in my face most of the time as we crawled on our bellies in the black dust under the hotel turning valves on while checking for leaks. Late in the afternoon when we were covered with dirt, John pointed to a new bright-orange valve and said, "I added it last year. The cedar posts that hold the hotel up are getting tired, like your Dad and me. As this old place sags, you're going to have to add more valves" since the pipes would sag along with hotel and need draining in new places.

His words but grazed my mind. I was young and excited about the upcoming summer. I didn't want to think about what it was like to get old; I just wanted to take a hot bath and hope my sore muscles would feel better in the morning. But today I see that John was telling me that he wasn't going to be around much longer.

Maybe I should have let Dad quit. He was getting older too. And when John was gone, another part of Dad's life, like Benny and Dario, would be missing.

I had never much thought about maintenance in the hotel. I figured the guests didn't care about it either. They weren't going to say that we did a good job turning on the water. John never got the praise Dario did standing next to his ice carvings on the Sunday night buffet. But, of course, I was terribly wrong. If the water wasn't properly turned on, the rooms would have been a wreck and there would have been no guests.

That evening I took a scalding bath. There in the tub, I remembered a hot-water line breaking in room 122 years earlier. Steam was spraying everywhere, the carpet felt like a swamp, and wallpaper was hanging halfway down the walls. Obviously John had been as important as Dario. And I could see why he liked a good drink. After spending the day slithering around under the hotel, I needed one, too.

The next day I continued my indoctrination into hotel maintenance by wandering around the buildings looking for leaks. Since pinhole breaks might not be noticeable at first, this was necessary to avoid big problems. John had always done this, but with me available he could now spend more time doing what he liked, drinking at the smoke-filled local bar.

As I walked by Dad's cubbyhole office just off the lobby, I realized that he'd be back from Florida in a few weeks. I worried as I thought about him coming home to a summer of work, not retirement. Was I doing the right thing? The thought continued to haunt me as I rambled around the dark halls of the hotel and didn't leave me until I stepped out into the sunshine on the back kitchen porch to a sight that brought a smile to my face. Across the gravel parking lot sat a long, white, one-story plywood building with little windows; the waitress dormitory—a building on which Dad had spared a lot of expense.

Pebbles crunched under my tennis shoes as I walked over to it. I climbed the front steps and unlocked the door which groaned open with rust.

Inside it smelled. Its walls, even after a winter of emptiness, were redolent with the odors of stale beer and cigarettes. With the electricity off, there was no light except for what daylight could filter in through two high, dirty windows. It took a while for my eyes to adjust to the darkness, then I could make out the writing on the walls in the entry room. Each year the girls would scribble all over these walls. It was usually harmless stuff about boyfriends and parties, but occasionally there were curses directed at Dad or Dario. For years John would paint over the writing each spring. But when John retired, except for turning the water off and on, Dad just gave up and left the graffiti.

I moved over to the far right corner of the room and bent down. Just below the yellowed window was scribbled a comment about one of the girls from the last summer spending her nights with me. I smiled. So much of my life, and my pleasures, had been tied to the hotel.

I stood, turned, and began inching my way down the dark, narrow hall leading toward the bedrooms. As I passed the doors, I listened for drips of water. There were none. The door to the fourth room on the right was ajar. I paused, then entered. Like all the others, it was boxcar-sized. It contained two narrow beds with curved metal headboards, and its plywood walls were painted light blue. Years ago John had purchased the paint for the lobby. But Mother had hated it, so John used it where it didn't matter, in the dorm.

When I lost my virginity in that room the summer before college, I hadn't noticed the color. All that mattered was the girl with her blonde hair tangled down to her waist.

The room looked the same as always, except with more marks on the walls where succeeding girls had tacked posters and pictures of boyfriends. My eyes drifted over to the foot of the bed where halfway up the wall faint sunlight from the adjacent room was shining through a half-dollar-sized hole. I remembered John telling me to fix it back in the spring of 1971. I never got around to it. Dad didn't care about the waitresses' privacy, so I skipped it. I hadn't figured that on a cool night in late August, I would wish that I had. The girls in the next room heard it all; the next morning the entire staff knew.

By a strange bit of coincidence, years before it had a hole in the wall, the room had been used by my summer girl, Annie. Actually she'd been my babysitter, but Mother thought it sounded more genteel to refer to her as a "summer girl." Since our moneyed neighbors had called their babysitters summer girls, so should we.

I thought back to how Dad used to pick the worst waitress to take care of me each summer. Inevitably they all turned out the same, lousy. I remember them sitting by the pool, chewing gum, reading romance novels, and writing letters to their boyfriends while I played by myself, ignored.

Then, when I was eight, Annie came along. She actually volunteered to trade places with the girl chosen for me. Her father had plenty of money to pay for her education, so she didn't need the tip money and didn't like being a waitress. Swimming, hiking, and biking sounded better to her.

Annie and I took long walks every day with Teddy Bear, my first Saint Bernard. One day when the leaves were flailing in a hot wind, we found a boardwalk heading toward a cedar forest. After a bit of hiking we stopped on a small log bridge over a mint-filled stream. We both knew it immediately; this was going to be our special place.

Annie sat down, pulling her long dark hair back into a ponytail. "This is perfect. Notice the light? Even the shadows have color. I wish I could paint it so we could have this moment forever."

Now closing the door, I remembered that Annie and I had spent a lot of time over that summer on that bridge talking about painting. She was a business major; her desire to paint must have been squelched. I wondered what had become of her.

Chapter 4

A black kitchen

In mid-May that spring of 1981, Mother and Dad returned from Florida. After a winter of golf and sitting on the beach, Dad was ready to kick ass. I'd been away at Michigan and Notre Dame for the last nine springs, arriving back in Harbor Springs after all the hard work had been done, so I'd forgotten what it was like to open the hotel. I think Dad wanted to make sure that his former college-boy son, who'd talked him out of retirement, remembered quickly.

It seemed that things happened much faster than when I was in high school. I felt that I was in a spring training camp for a football team. Within a week of his arrival, the maintenance staff and I had the pool drained, acid scrubbed, painted, and filled. Then within another week we'd trimmed all the hedges, planted all the geraniums, and put up the green-and-white striped canopy over the bare entrance-frame.

One morning in early June a few days before the hotel opened, when the dew was still on the flowers, I walked across the grounds from my suite. I headed toward Dad's office in the main inn and nodded at the new groundskeeper pushing the mower. He was doing okay, but I sensed that Dad wouldn't like it. Since John wasn't cutting it, Dad would probably say that the grass was being mowed unevenly and edged rough. I sniffed the air. The smell of fresh-mown grass, of newness, brought a feeling that summer was about to begin, that everything was all right in the world. It was as when I was a kid playing with my toy dump truck on the hotel lawn after John had mowed. I felt a premonition that good things were going to happen, that this was going to be the most important summer of my life.

I was hoping that Dad was finally going to let me reorganize the front desk and the hotel's method of taking reservations. Like all hotels, the Colonial Inn regularly accepted more reservations than it had rooms available. But also like all hoteliers, Dad banked on the almost certain knowledge that some of the people who made reservations weren't going to show up. This generally had been an acceptable gamble because Dad was good at estimating the relatively small percentage of cancellations. So in most cases, with the help of some luck, we came out evenly with a full house—the perfect situation, which Dad loved to brag about.

But in recent years the percentage of no-shows had greatly increased, making Dad's guessing game more risky and more likely to result in serious trouble for the hotel. This increase had been exasperated by the resort children and grandchildren having to vie over use of the family cottage—there were just too many of them now. With uncertainty as to whether they would even be able to stay at their cottage, it had lately become a common practice for them to book a backup reservation at the Colonial Inn as insurance, in the event a more desirable second cousin beat them out of their family cottage. Why not? It cost nothing if they didn't need the room, and they saw this as necessary because the more favorable heir may not bother to inform them until the last minute. Being rich means there's no hurry to make decisions.

At any rate it was a miserable experience to tell a would-be guest that there were no rooms available. I remembered walking by the front desk while some chagrined desk clerk would tell a guest that we simply couldn't honor their reservation and that we'd booked them a room at some lesser hotel. Dad always knew his competitors' situation and where, if necessary, he could send his overflow, or "dump them off," as Dad, who wanted to be known as the gracious host, would sometimes say when his back was to the wall and he was sure no one would overhear him. Dad, like a good hotel man, always had an ace in the hole.

Even Dad's worst rivals were happy to aid him because they could never tell when the situation could be reversed. Dad would always leave the task of telling folks with a reservation that there were no rooms to one of his minions. He may have personally avoided the turmoil, but that potential guest was never going to return and probably tell at least ten other people never to stay with us. I thought of a couple some years earlier whose reservation hadn't been honored. They were so mad that they charged a full dinner, cocktails, and an exorbitant tip to a fictitious room, then left. Dad was furious, but in my opinion he deserved it, just like the time another couple had refused to leave, opting to spend the night on the front porch rather than going to another hotel.

I wanted to change all that by requiring potential guests to guarantee their reservations with a credit card. By 1980 this was a somewhat common practice, but Dad, like most old-time hoteliers, didn't even take credit cards. I wasn't sure if it was because he considered them to be low rent or because he didn't want to pay the fees. Regardless, we didn't take credit cards and, in my opinion, our unnecessary overbooking situation was becoming worse each year.

Further, the number of bad accounts was going up since the number of new guests was radically increasing and we had no way of investigating these people before extending credit. In the past Dad had been excellent at sizing people up, but now the task was too overwhelming even for him. He no longer had the time to call references on each new guest and it simply wasn't practical. We needed to begin guaranteeing our rooms with credit cards, but I wasn't sure if Dad was ready.

A few minutes later, I reached the hotel and was standing in front of Dad's big desk. He sat leaning back in his cane chair, balanced on its back legs. He did this so often that the sides of the chair were worn from rubbing against the bottom of his desk.

I was about ready to start discussing my ideas when Dad looked straight up at me. "You've got to move out of your suite before we open. I need it."

I stood there staring at him, thinking that I hadn't even had a chance to say anything yet. The waves of his silver hair were almost touching the wall behind him. Damn, I was quickly forgetting about my plans for reorganizing the office and accepting credit cards. The important thing was that I had really grown to like that room. It would have been a perfect bachelor pad, something I would have put to use once the college girls arrived.

"You can either move back into our cottage or take a room over the kitchen."

Over the kitchen? That's where the cooks lived. Was that what he thought of me now, just equal to a cook? I wasn't even going to get Dario's apartment; the new chef was getting that. Those rooms were small. Teddy Bear was now nine months old. It'd be a tight squeeze.

When I complained, he snapped, "You know, I should have sold when I had the chance."

I studied him. Moving back home to the cottage and being under his ongoing supervision wasn't an option. I'd live with the bacon grease, I told him.

Except for having been rebuffed when I'd asked to take that long-term reservation from the woman in Naples, Dad and I hadn't discussed anything since December, when I had offered to run the hotel. I'd hoped that by his agreeing to my coming home and working for him during the summer, he'd tacitly agreed to me becoming the manager.

The only money that I had had came from renting out the hotel rooms during the past winter. It hadn't been too bad, about ten thousand dollars, a good portion of which I had stashed away. But I felt far from secure. Before now I hadn't wanted to risk upsetting Dad by bringing up my situation. But since Dad had brought up my accommodations, now seemed like a good time to discuss things.

"I'll move over the kitchen, but could we talk about what I'll be doing this summer and what I'll be paid?"

"Well, you can be the maitre d' again and pitch in wherever I need you, housekeeping, the cocktail lounge, kitchen. We'll talk about the money in the fall. Let's see how the season turns out."

I managed a faint smile. Dad hadn't mentioned the front desk or reservations, and he'd given his standard answer to any employee asking for a raise. Usually the season didn't turn out too good, and Dad didn't pay any more. Had I made a mistake? At least the law firm back in Chicago gave me a steady paycheck.

Two days after the hotel opened, around seven in the morning, I was asleep in my room over the kitchen when Dad pounded on my door. He was always at work early because he felt a good hotel man had to be. "A disaster could happen at any hour," he'd say.

I awoke, stared for a few long seconds at the ceiling where the cracks looked like they were expanding, then bolted up to open the door. Dad stood there, the veins on his face bulging. "They're gone . . ."

The new chef and his entire crew had snuck out during the night. The hotel wasn't for them. Having worked at a private country club with limited hours, they hadn't realized how much work there would be at our hotel, and Dad probably hadn't told them. He assumed that everyone in the business knew they had to work three meals a day, seven days a week.

I followed Dad down the narrow back stairs to the kitchen, where almost every board creaked, where the smells of sizzling bacon and sausage should have been in the air. There were no smells. I looked around at the first waitresses beginning to punch in at the time clock. They were giggling. I realized then that I had on only a bathrobe.

But I had a bigger problem; the kitchen was black, an old hotel term meaning that there were no cooks. Breakfast would start in an hour if there was someone to cook it. My God, that'd probably be me. Who else was there?

Dad walked over to the kitchen stoves, turned back toward me, and raised his voice. I could see the sweat breaking out on his temples as he began. "If I hadn't listened to you, I'd be on the golf course. I knew it'd be impossible to go on without Dario."

"That isn't fair."

"Who cares about fairness?" Dad shot back. "This is my hotel and you're ruining it."

Silence consumed the kitchen as the girls stopped chattering. A drop of cold water fell on my head, condensation from an exposed water line hanging from the kitchen ceiling. Dad had never cared much about spending money on things that the guests didn't see. If a water line broke in the kitchen, he'd just replace it with a new line hung wherever John thought convenient. Dad wasn't going to bust out walls in the kitchen looking for a water leak.

"Goddamn it," I said. "You hired the asshole, not me. It's like you wanted things not to go well so you could prove that you were right in wanting to quit."

Dad hadn't wasted a lot of time in hiring the now-departed new chef. He talked to his golfing buddies in Florida who suggested one from a neighboring club. After Dad sampled his shrimp scampi, he was hired and told to bring the rest of his kitchen crew. It was incredulous that Dad hadn't spent time getting to know his new chef. Maybe he could have had lunch a few times with him. Maybe he could have talked to his crew. Maybe he could have called the manager of the golf club where he worked. But Dad had done none of those things. With Dario and Benny gone, I wondered how Dad could have been so careless.

"It wouldn't have mattered. Dario can't be replaced. Let me tell you something; the good lord himself couldn't duplicate him."

"Oh, good God. He doesn't have to be duplicated; just find another dependable chef. There are lots of hotels that have good chefs who don't walk out. It can't be that hard."

"You haven't learned a damn thing."

"Give me a chance, I'll show you."

"Let me tell you something," said Dad, his voice softening a bit. "It's not that easy. It's hard to keep a staff when we're only open ten weeks. We offer nothing—no permanence. Dario and Benny didn't care. They were old, like me and the hotel. This hotel has no future. Think of how many of our long-term guests are gone."

He was right. By the beginning of 1980, guests were no longer staying for the whole season, leaving many vacant room nights. Harbor Springs, like other resort towns, had experienced its share of growth. Around the outskirts of the town on cheap land, condominiums and golfing communities were sprouting up out of nowhere and, much to the chagrin of the old-moneyed people, they were all trading on the name of Harbor Springs. Even today the internet advertises condominiums, hotels and homes as if they're right in Harbor Springs though they may be miles away. The name is powerful.

As our all-season guests died off, new potential long-term guests were no longer content to be relegated to the space of a mere hotel room. The Colonial Inn had been operated on a culture of service which no longer seemed to be important to new retirees. It had become a question of price and square footage, and we were losing the battle.

I looked away. "I'm sorry. I'll try to be the chef till you can get a replacement."

"I'll get a couple of dishwashers to help you. Hell, things can't get any worse."

Dad turned and stomped out of the kitchen. I thought for moment. Had I blown it? Would Dad now call the real estate developer?

Thinking back, I can see that he didn't really blame me for the crew's disappearance. He just needed to vent. He knew that he'd hired the wrong people, but couldn't admit it. How many fathers can tell their sons that they've made a mistake? Years later, after having made a lifetime of employment decisions myself, I realize that Dad had just come to an age where it was painful to hire new people.

Dad was headstrong in making decisions. He'd jump right in, often without considering consequences, like the one and only time he went skiing.

I was eight-years old. Skiing was in its infancy in Northern Michigan, and Dad thought that he might be able to make some big money in it, so he decided that we'd stay up north till Christmas. This was an adventure because our summer cottage wasn't built for the cold weather. One night our water pipes froze and John, who'd had a bit too much to drink, almost burnt the place down thawing the pipes with a torch. But this didn't matter because Dad wanted to look into the ski business.

Dad and a former Norwegian Army ski officer he'd befriended, a man who claimed to have eaten boiled earthworms during World War II, had a plan. Somehow they had talked their way into obtaining options on an abandoned ski hill.

One day just before Christmas when the snow had come down nice and thick, Dad decided that we'd actually go skiing. He wanted to check out his nearest competitor, Boyne Mountain. But it wasn't his competition; he didn't even own a ski resort. But Dad had talked about it so much that he felt like he did—or at least he'd have one soon. "Five dollars a lift ticket and a thousand people—that's enough for a new Cadillac just in one day," he said.

Dad watched as Mother and I had a lesson from an Austrian instructor, who taught us how to use the rope-tow on the beginner hill and to keep our knees bent. Then he went off to show us how skiing was really done. Dad had been a good football player, an athlete in his slimmer years, so a lesson seemed a waste to him. Mother and I watched as his body filled the red two-seat chairlift and saw it swing from side to side as it made its way, dodging pine trees, to the top of the highest hill. I imagined Dad talking to himself as he approached the summit. How high is it? How hard could skiing be? You just put the damn skis on, make a few turns and go down the hill. No big thing!

As Mother and I held our breath, Dad learned the meaning of vertical drop. His guardian angel hadn't been asleep that morning when he went straight down the tournament hill with his gray overcoat flying and his skis shaking. He should have been carrying a briefcase. Reaching the bottom, he screeched across the icy parking lot and slammed into a snow bank, miraculously unhurt. Years later, a black diamond, indicating a ski trail of advanced difficulty, would mark his route.

Swearing with every word imaginable, he came over to where Mother and I were standing. Dad put his arm around mother. "Skiing is dangerous! We're going home. You could get really hurt. This isn't for sane people; it's serious stuff."

It didn't matter that we'd had a lesson and learned how to go down our little hill without falling; it was time to go.

A few minutes after learning that I was going to have to cook, I was standing behind the steam table in white golf shirt and khaki pants trying to light the gas pilots on the ancient cast-iron stoves. Dario had been able to light them effortlessly, but I was having a miserable time. It took ten minutes and several burnt fingers before I was able to get them lit. This didn't bode well for my career as chef.

Lighting the pilots on the stoves was one thing; now I had to actually use them. I stood there looking at the battery of ranges like I was a medieval knight appraising his enemies in preparing to do battle. Wondering how I could fill Dario's shoes, I tensed, realizing that I would have to fill the whole cooking staff's shoes. At least it would only be temporary, until Dad could hire new cooks, I told myself.

I had learned some of Dario's secrets, but I certainly wasn't prepared to be a chef. What would I do? I had to cook breakfast, plan something for lunch, get ready for the main dinner, and lay out forty lamb shanks for a private party. And I'd never cooked a lamb shank before.

After a few minutes of staring at the stoves I decided that it might help if I at least looked like a chef. Even if it didn't convince anyone else, it might at least give me a little confidence. Dario had always taken a lot of effort in dressing like a professional chef. "You got to be different—wear things that make you stand out from the other cooks; let the folks know that you're the one."

Back in Dario's office I found a white double-breasted chef's coat and Dario's gold-and-black checkered hat. I'd wear them and look like a real chef. As I put them on, I thought, hell, I'll pull this off. I'll carry the whole damn kitchen just like Dario and Benny did back in '69, when the rest of the kitchen crew had walked out. This would be my big challenge. I'd show Dad and make Dario and Benny proud. Damn, it didn't matter that I'd have to do this with only two inexperienced dishwashers.

A few minutes after eight o'clock, I was slowly frying, poaching, and scrambling eggs. The orders were stacking up, and my coat had a big yellow stain from an egg that hit me instead of the frying pan. The dishwashers were no help. They couldn't boil water. Now I wasn't quite as confident as I had been back in the chef's office. Why couldn't all the guests eat scrambled eggs?

That afternoon Allen Silverstein walked into the kitchen. I was reading a cookbook spread open on a carving table strewn with piles of vegetables, potatoes, and lamb shanks. My apron was covered with tomato, carrot, lamb's blood, and other stains.

Allen's grandparents had begun coming to the hotel around 1910. He and his parents had spent every summer with us when I was a child, but he hadn't come in the years since his father had died. Maybe he'd been embarrassed. His father had died shortly after returning home from his last summer at the hotel, leaving the bill for the entire summer vacation unpaid.

If Dad had taken credit cards, this awkward situation would never have happened. The credit card company, not Dad, would have been the one to collect from Allen's mother. But since that wasn't the case, Dad ended up with a mahogany speedboat in lieu of payment. It had been a somewhat fair trade, but I wondered if Allen had stayed away from the hotel all these years because he hadn't felt right about it. Regardless, all that had been forgotten two days earlier when Allen had returned and Dad had put his big arms around him.

Allen, now in his forties and a successful pharmaceutical representative, had come back to connect with his past. He looked around the empty kitchen, probably missing his old friends Dario and Benny, then stared down at my apron. "I didn't know you were a chef."

"Neither did I."

Allen reached over the carving table and shook my hand, ignoring the lamb's blood there. Because time was short, I kept on prepping the lamb shanks while I told him what had happened and that I'd never planned on being a chef. In fact, I was damned scared. If Dad didn't find another chef soon, I might ruin his season and end up permanently disfigured from a slip of a knife or an enormous splatter of sizzling grease.

Allen looked at me and asked, "You've got to try. Remember that trout?"

When I was a little boy, he, John, and I had tried for weeks one summer to catch a big trout that had been lurking off the end of the hotel dock. I smiled. "It was in the afternoon after my first day of kindergarten, just after you left that we finally got him. I'd had a horrible time because I hated school and didn't want to be away from the hotel. John and I stayed down at the dock till it almost got dark, but we caught that damn fish."

"Well, you're back at the hotel again now; don't give up. Make the food wonderful, something you can be proud of."

Great advice, I thought; if I only knew how to do it.

It was unsettling to see Mother walk into the kitchen in her high heels and evening gown that night. She shook her head and left without any words of encouragement.

At the time I felt hurt. I was pitching in, doing my best for the hotel, but she didn't seem to care. I knew she was only worried about what people at her club would say. She had bragged about my prestigious college degrees. Now I'd turned out to be a cook.

But today I can understand. It had been only five years since Mother had hosted a book signing party for her old friend Sonny Hemingway, who had penned a biography of her famous brother, Ernest. The front-porch affair had come just a few days after Sonny's appearance on the *Today Show* with Gene Shalit, where she'd sheared off a lock of his hair. Mother had invited everyone, including a couple who had stayed at the hotel the previous summer while they were building their new cottage. Although quite wealthy, these folks weren't connected to the area so mother had taken it upon herself to introduce them socially. During that past summer, Mother had thrown them a get-acquainted party at the pool: a piano player, Caesar salad, lobster cocktail, chateaubriand, and flaming bananas foster.

About a month after the Hemingway party, the now-socially-connected couple hosted a big party for their house guests, President Gerald Ford and his wife Betty. Mother and Dad weren't invited. I'm sure that she must have searched for reasons, possibly coming to the conclusion that being hoteliers didn't cut it. So watching me become a cook wouldn't have been comforting.

Five days later I was still cooking. Following Allen's advice about persevering, trying to remember everything that Dario had taught me, and reading a lot of *Escoffier* and Julia Child, I was getting by. Although it was hard to see when I was young, Dario had said that cooking would always be part of my life.

But I was having a finger-burning time sautéing shrimp scampi, broiling white fish almandine, and baking chicken divan all at the same time. Something had to be done. Anyone following a cookbook can prepare a great meal, but only a chef can produce varieties of mouth-watering cuisine at the same time. At that time, I was far from being a chef.

Dario had shared many of his recipes and techniques with me, but that training had served only to help satisfy my love of good food and impress sorority girls back at the University of Michigan. I had never shared the inferno behind the range with him when the kitchen was busy, actually putting out vast quantities of gourmet food. I wasn't sure how he browned off a rack of lamb in its last minute under an orange-hot boiler while sautéing five orders of tenderloin bordelaise and poaching lemon sole without burning all of them.

That evening during my nightly battle with the stoves, I dropped an order of shrimp scampi, which splashed sizzling wine-butter on my wrist. After howling words worse than any drunken sailor, I decided that something had to be done if I was going to survive with my body intact until Dad could find a new chef. At the end of the dinner, sitting on the steps of the back porch, holding a rag filled with ice around my wrist, I saw that my only hope was to drastically reduce the volume of cooked-to-order food.

I'd have to come up with a couple of specialties that could be roasted in the afternoon, then thrown back into the oven for a few minutes by my ex-dishwashers before serving.

Dario's signature dish, duckling à la orange, was going to be one of them. It had always been my favorite; tasty, even elegant. It stimulated the taste buds and created the illusion of being something difficult to prepare. In 1980 few restaurants served it and not many home-cooks prepared it, yet it was easy.

Dario had joked that a good duck only needed lots of booze and plenty of cooking. He was right, but there were a few other things. The duck needs to be marinated in Grand Marnier and orange concentrate for several hours, then placed upside-down on a rack in a roasting pan so the bottom fat slowly flavors its way through the meat. Then, after an hour, it should be turned right-side-up and be covered with a loose tinfoil tent so it can breathe. Then it should be slow-roasted for several more hours while frequently basted with its drippings. In final minutes the duck needs to be liberally doused with Grand Marnier and the skin crisped under a full-blast oven. The skin on a well-cooked duck is deliciously intoxicating.

As with everything else he prepared, Dario was never clear as to exact times. They varied with the oven and how many ducks were being cooked. A good chef just had to know those things. But, surprisingly, in just a week I was getting a good feel for it.

The sauce was another thing. Dario had a way of boiling orange peels, then cutting them into thin strips and adding them to simmered orange juice, sugar, and Grand Marnier. But I couldn't get it right. My orange peels were downright bitter. I didn't have time to fool with the damn things, so I just added orange marmalade to orange concentrate and Grand Marnier.

To be sure that the duck was a success, I decided to do something different. My duck would be flaming. Bacardi 151-proof rum, once flamed, doesn't do anything to the taste of the duck. The rum erupts into fire at the touch of a match. A waitress could spoon a little of it over the duck and light it before serving, creating a show. Dario had always said that presentation was the most important part of fine cooking. He'd have been pleased. Further, I'd be putting even more booze on the duck, which would have delighted him as well.

My next specialty was going to be braised lamb shank. Why not? It sounded positively medieval and was something that would excite the palates of our guests. It had gone over wonderfully at the private party my first night of being chef, so I knew I could cook it.

The next night I placed a perfectly browned duck, garnished with a scalloped orange, and a thick meaty lamb shank surrounded by asparagus and baby ears of corn on silver trays atop the entrance table in the dining room. Then, while I still had time to be out front before the orders started, I went around the dining room. "Have you seen my duck? Beautifully browned isn't it? At noon I was rubbing it with cracked pepper and coarse salt. To get that color, you can't take your eyes off it. You know, we flambé it . . . And the lamb shank, that had to be watched too. It's got just a bit of crust to it, just right. And I've got a great mint sauce for it."

The dining room opened at seven o'clock, and by eight-fifteen twenty-four orders of ducks had been flambéd and twenty lamb shanks served. We were sold out of both. When I walked into the dining room to apologize for running out, I was hailed as a victor of the kitchen by one table after the next.

As I reached the row of tables next to the French-paned windows where our more important hotel guests dined, a wrinkled lady puffing on a cigarette grabbed my arm and in a voice made harsh by her smoking said, "That's the best Goddamn duck I've ever had, better than Petite Marmite in Palm Beach." She looked like she didn't often swear, so I took it to mean that my duck was exceptional.

A few tables down, a party of four sat with bare bones in front of them like they had just finished a feast with Henry VIII. "The lamb shanks . . ." they exclaimed almost in unison. "We've never had them before; the sauce . . ."

Seeing Dad nearby and knowing that he was overhearing, I bent down toward the people, but raised my voice. "Ah, you must have noticed the Saint-Émilion that I used to reduce the lamb juices."

Everyone nodded. What else could they do? Admit that they hadn't detected this intricacy?

I gave them a big cheek-to-cheek smile, like Dario used to do when he went into dining room to receive compliments. "A lot of chefs will use a table Bordeaux in their reduction of drippings into sauce, but I've always felt that it was worthwhile to use the good stuff. Did you notice the tarragon that I had rubbed into the shanks before cooking?"

Damn, I was really laying it on. Actually, an expensive wine doesn't make any difference, but, hell, it sure sounded better. I hadn't gone into the dining room to receive compliments, but I was enjoying it. I glanced up. Dad, wearing his maraschino-red jacket, who had been surveying the dining room with his usual patriarchal benevolence, was now standing at a nearby table. His head was inclined graciously as he accepted compliments on my food, so I stepped it up.

"Did you like the mint sauce? It's made with real mint leaves. I picked them out of our creek. Wine vinegar gives it just the right amount of tartness. Mint jelly is fine for lamb chops, but a lamb shank deserves a mint sauce—more tart."

I had just learned to make the sauce from a cookbook less than a week before, but they didn't know that. Damn, I was sounding like a chef and actually beginning to feel like one.

"Tim's quite the chef, isn't he?" boomed Dad, putting his arm around my shoulders. How would he know? Dad wouldn't even have known how to begin to roast a prime rib. All he'd ever done was stand next to Dario and accept compliments. And now he was standing next to me accepting them.

"He's worked with Dario for years. It really shows, don't you think?"

Worked with Dario? All I'd done was master a few sauces and help him some afternoons. Much of what I had learned had required a lot of filling in the blanks. Although a great chef, Dario was a man of few words and much improvising. Every time he made his cheese spread, something that he was known for, the ingredients and quantities changed. "Cheddar cheese, a few herbs and spices, enough beer to soften it, a cup or two of horseradish, a small amount Worcester sauce, and a few squirts of Tabasco," he would say with a wink.

I now lowered my head, trying to act a bit modest, if that was possible in this situation. Now a number of guests were nodding approval.

Later that night I was sitting at the bar relishing my success at attempting to be a chef. How long could I pull it off? The guests wouldn't keep ordering only lamb shanks and duck. As I pondered what to do next, Dad walked in and sat next to me.

He ordered a martin, lit a Camel, and took a couple of long drags. "I can't find a chef. That's the problem with opening so late. It's now July; the good ones already have jobs. You want to do it the rest of the summer?"

I took a gulp of my martin like it was a watered-down gin and tonic, not straight alcohol. What was Dad thinking? Tonight had been fun, but I was no chef.

"You can do it," said Dad, knocking the ashes off his cigarette onto his cocktail napkin. He wasn't one to care whether there was an ashtray nearby.

I looked down at the burn on my wrist from the scampi butter the night before. "Yeah, if we only served precooked items."

Dad leaned back in his chair. "We'll do that. It'll be your baby. I need you."

He needed me now. I thought back to when he had asked me to move out of my suite a few weeks before. Maybe being the chef wouldn't be so bad after all.

I raised my eyebrows. "Could I have Dario's apartment?"

It was still over the kitchen, but it had a separate living room and three windows that looked out on the hotel grounds, an improvement over the cubicle I now occupied with one window over the garbage hopper. I'd be able to sleep without having Teddy Bear snoring next to me. And for a second I thought about how it might be an acceptable place to bring a girl. But then I remembered that I'd be cooking three meals a day, seven days a week, with little time.

Dad leaned forward and took a quick puff on his cigarette. "Hell, you can move to Dario's apartment tonight. I've got to have goddamned good food. I don't care what you have to do with the menu."

I looked over at Dad. His cigarette was burnt down to its end, yet he held it there just centimeters from his lips, waiting to take a final puff, and I knew he couldn't do it until I answered. It was nice to have the upper hand. I'd already been thinking about other possibilities, like prime rib au jus, braised short ribs jardinière, shrimp au gratin, and white fish baked in chardonnay butter, all of which could be prepared in advance; all well and good. But instead of being snuggled up with a college girl at night, I'd be with Julia Child.

But Dad didn't care about my pleasures, pains, or long-term plans. He just wanted good food. So I just said, "I'll have many items cooked in advance. We won't run out." I rubbed the burn on my wrist. "But I'll have to do away with the sautéed stuff. Is that okay?"

"Fine. We make our money off the hotel rooms anyway. I don't care about the cost. And for that matter, I'll give you Dario's salary. Just make it happen."

Damn. I couldn't believe it; twenty thousand dollars. That was a small fortune for ten weeks of work in 1980, more than I would have made in a whole year at the law firm. Sometimes a lucky break comes disguised! Like putting too much tarragon in the Béarnaise sauce only to discover it's improved the flavor.

But what was Dad thinking? Through the big salary was he trying to help me accumulate money to one day buy the hotel? Was my arrangement going to become permanent, or was he still thinking of calling the real estate developer? Was this a test to see if I had the requisite grit, or was he really just desperate for a chef? I wasn't sure. Even now looking back, I'm still not sure. The man who had left home at sixteen with a carpetbag is still difficult to analyze.

CHAPTER 5

I WANT MY STOLI

A week after officially becoming the chef, a title I was still adjusting to, I was making my nightly rounds through our white-linen dining room, discussing cuisine. I was beginning to relish this part of my new job. Never before, as a maitre d' or lawyer, did I feel so important. The guests seemed to want my opinion on important matters, like how much tarragon to put in the Béarnaise or how long to roast lamb shanks.

In the corner of the dining room where the French-paned windows came together, sat Mrs. Catherine C. Baldwin, one of the last of our all-season guests. Her gray hair styled back just enough to cover her hearing aid, she looked like a courtier. Coming to the hotel since before I was born, she embodied what the hotel had once been.

I quickly nodded as I walked by, not wanting to get trapped by her stories about people who were dead. It wouldn't have mattered to her that the dining room was beginning to fill and that I had pans of whitefish baking. But I wasn't fast enough. Peering at me through her tortoise shell glasses, she'd already begun. "I never have the same waitress. These girls don't understand. I want my Stoli as soon as I sit down."

She pointed her long finger at her empty glass. "I always have two."

I'd forgotten to assign her a permanent waitress, maybe because I'd been overwhelmed in my new world of cooking or maybe because

I'd simply dreaded it. She'd complained constantly about her waitress the previous summer, yet refused to change. That girl was an airhead, she claimed, knew nothing about classical literature, put too much ice in her Stoli, and made her sundaes too big.

"I'll get you another Stoli. Tomorrow I'll see about finding you a waitress."

I thought of how Dario had called her every single morning to discuss her dinner options, anything special that she might want. Hell, I was trying to avoid cooked-to-order items. I'd given no thought to special requests.

I walked back into the steamy kitchen, the air filled with the scents of olive oil, oregano, and fish. As I began helping the dishwashers-cum-cooks, I thought of Mrs. Baldwin sitting out in the air-conditioned dining room alone. I felt sad for her. It was an odd feeling for me. I'd never much thought about someone else being lonely. It was a shame that she was spending the last years of her life alone, desperate for someone to talk with.

Looking back, I realize that previous winter I'd had too many nights sitting by the fire with only a Saint Bernard and a martin for company. I hadn't realized it then, but that desolate winter had opened up my heart. I had become able to appreciate what a person feels like alone in the world—or in a restaurant. I could now understand why Mrs. Baldwin read a book during dinner and why she studied her menu long after she'd ordered.

At the time I couldn't comprehend why, but I knew there was something endearing about Mrs. Baldwin, something about the way she looked at me—something that said she could be a real friend. Call it insight or call it intuition, but I felt it. I hadn't noticed it before, but maybe I hadn't needed a friend before. In all my previous ten summers at the hotel, the guests, even Mrs. Baldwin, had been a blur. I was drinking, chasing girls, and planning on getting rich as a lawyer. Summers weren't real; they were just a time to play. I had no time to look for friendship, especially from a white-haired lady like Mrs. Baldwin.

There, standing in the greasy steam behind the range, I vowed to find Mrs. Baldwin a waitress who'd actually listen to her and not turn her back and walk away like girls had done in past years. Mrs. Baldwin's waitress, whoever she was, would have to be willing to make less money. Listening to Mrs. Baldwin occupied a lot of time, so she wouldn't be able to wait on as many tables. But it was a good trade-off because Mrs.

Baldwin never ate breakfast or lunch in the dining room, so her waitress was excused from those hard-work, low-tipped meals.

I ran through the girls in my mind. No one jumped out. I didn't know them well since I was spending most of my waking hours in the kitchen. I thought of my old summer girl, Anne. She'd have been perfect, but that was twenty years ago. I'd have to talk to the girls to learn more about them.

The next morning I sat in the back corner of the dining room as the waitresses were closing down breakfast. I sipped a cup of hot tea with fresh lemon as I watched them scurrying about in their crisp white uniforms filling sugar bowls, syrup pitchers and folding napkins. One with long pony-tailed red hair seemed to be in a hurry, like she wanted out. I liked the cute little way she crinkled up nose as she called out to the other girls to get moving. Even hidden under her fits-all uniform the curves of her body, as much as I tried not to stare, suddenly began to intrigue me. Possibly she might be someone who would like to skip breakfast and lunch.

"What's the hurry?" I said, noticing her prolific freckles. She was someone with initiative—someone who wouldn't get pushed around. She was also a pretty girl, maybe twenty, and I sensed from her sunburn, she liked the outdoors.

"I've got lunch off. It's a gorgeous day. I don't want to waste any of it, got to get to my bike. I can get at least forty miles in. I'm going to do the Tour de France someday."

Her long legs were smooth, her muscles taut . . . I couldn't stop looking at her. It had been a long winter in Harbor Springs alone with a Saint Bernard, and I was only twenty-seven.

I asked her to sit for just a moment, and we talked. Jennifer was a western girl who attended the University of Colorado, near her dad's ranch. She was majoring in literature and wanted to be a writer.

As we talked across the small dining table, I became aware of her closeness and a faint fragrant smell of strawberries. Was it some kind of perfume or had she been eating them? It didn't matter. I had honestly been looking for a waitress for Mrs. Baldwin, but now out of nowhere, I suddenly wanted this outdoors girl. I worried that she might sense my loneliness, my desire, and be put off by it. But she was perfect, and I couldn't help staring at her.

A few minutes later when I ran out of small talk our conversation was about to end. I'd failed to even mention Mrs. Baldwin because I'd been so preoccupied wondering what she might be thinking about a twenty-seven-year-old guy wearing a chef's coat who was obviously coming on to her. I glanced down at the table realizing that she was young and there would be all kinds of college boys in Harbor Springs for her to pick from this summer. I was destined, I saw, for a summer of only cooking duck.

There was a bit of silence, then she piped up, "Do you want to ride with me?"

"Yes!"

"We can ride up to Wilderness Beach and have a picnic. It's about thirty miles each way. Can you do it?

I wondered if she meant was I able to take that much time off or was I physically able to do it. I hadn't ridden my bike much in the last couple of years, but it didn't matter; I was going to Wilderness Beach if it killed me.

"I can do it."

"You're probably sick of cooking, so I'll pack our lunch. See you in twenty minutes."

I hadn't taken a meal off since becoming the chef, but I would now. My former dishwashers were good enough to handle things, and if they weren't, it didn't matter. I was going.

All the way along the Lake Michigan coast, up and down hills, thick with the dusty summer smell of pine needles, I tried to hide my exhaustion. I hadn't done anything like this since high school, but I was somewhat in condition from a winter of rigorous skiing.

When we finally reached the beach, she pulled out a red-and-white-checked table cloth from her back pack and spread it on the sand. Then she unscrewed the cap from a bottle of cheap white wine, took a gulp, and offered me the bottle. It wasn't bad. Then came lunch—steak tartare, a big glob of uncooked ground beef with spices and bread crumbs. She didn't have a kitchen in the dorm. If I knew she was going to feed me raw beef I would have offered to let her use the hotel kitchen to cook the damn meat.

I was hungry, but I was hungry for her as well. The sweat glistening on her neck from the long hot ride was too much. I stared at her yellow soaked bandana, now tied around her arm, allowing her thick hair to flow wildly. Unthinking, I shoved some of the steak tartare into my mouth and guzzled some wine to wash it down.

She laughed. "You're not supposed to eat it like that, silly." Instead she made a small ball and slowly put it in her mouth, sucking at it. "It's kind of like eating sheep's nuts. You take it slowly and suck it."

"Eating what?"

"Rocky Mountain oysters. We eat them all the time out in Colorado. They're especially good after a hard day of skiing. You never had them before?"

I thought she was quite a girl; raw meat and sheep's nuts. I couldn't help thinking what it would be like to be with her, believing this was a girl who wouldn't hold back on anything. The hell with Mrs. Baldwin; I wanted her for me.

"What are you staring at?" she said.

"You."

"Well then, do something. Out in Colorado we don't just stand there looking at each other. There's nobody around and, if there is, the hell with it."

Sometime later that afternoon when the sun was hanging a bit lower and we'd awakened from a nap on the beach, Jennifer offered me dessert, a piece of white cake with almond frosting that looked strangely like frozen cakes that I had ordered for the hotel. When she saw the inquisitive look on my face Jennifer blushed, making her freckles even more noticeable.

There followed a few seconds of silence, then a girlish giggle escaped from her widening smile. "Well, I didn't think I was going to be sleeping with the boss when the other waitresses and I threw those cakes out of the pantry window. The bushes below were a great place to hide them till we got off work."

Finding it impossible to be mad, I simply said, "How many cakes did you guys throw out the window?"

She hung her head and looked like she was pretending to be sorry. "Only ten, but there were a few pies. We had some great parties in the dorm."

I grabbed her and kissed her hard, but vowed to myself that in future years I would never have waitresses unpack pantry supplies again.

On the way home I told her about Mrs. Baldwin needing a permanent waitress, but added that I'd find someone else if she didn't want to do it.

"Why?" she asked.

"I don't want to force anything on you."

She stopped her bike and looked out over a cliff at the white caps far below on Lake Michigan. I brought my bike up next to her, wondering what the afternoon had meant to her. Had she felt sorry for me being stuck as a chef or did she like me? I wasn't sure.

After a moment of us both gazing out at lake, she leaned over and lightly kissed me on the cheek. "I'll be her waitress if we can have more biking afternoons."

Then she pulled away and her lips lightened, revealing a new sense of seriousness. "I'm going back to college in the fall, so that's all it's going to be."

I felt like she was giving me a business proposition. We'd be lovers for the summer and that was it. Despite that pleasing prospect, I felt vaguely disappointed. I'd never entered a relationship with a predetermined end before. But I wanted her, and her offer was one I couldn't refuse. Later, after relationships with other women who weren't as straightforward, I came to more fully appreciate Jennifer's honesty.

I nodded. She reached over across her bike, put her head to my face, and kissed me.

That night I took Jennifer over to Mrs. Baldwin's corner table.

"That's a lovely pink dress," said Jennifer to Mrs. Baldwin.

"Forget the flattery. Can I have crab tonight?"

I nodded to Jennifer that it could be arranged as I kept some Alaskan king crab legs in the freezer.

But Jennifer stared back at Mrs. Baldwin. "That was down-right rude. I paid you a compliment. I wasn't sucking up. I really do like your dress; it reminds me of my grandmother."

Mrs. Baldwin flushed, the effect heightening her still statuesque beauty as she set her cocktail glass down. The ice cubes clinked as her glass hit the table. "You really do like my dress?"

Jennifer nodded, her red hair swaying. There was something about this girl that entranced me, whether she was telling Mrs. Baldwin off or rolling in the sand with me.

"I think you and I are going to be friends. You have spunk and I like that," said Mrs. Baldwin. "It's a man's world, and a woman has to be tough just to survive. Sit down. I don't care about ordering yet. We need to talk."

Protocol aside, I violated all of Dad's rules, pulled out a chair for Jennifer, and went back to the kitchen. Mrs. Baldwin needed someone to talk to, and that was a hell of a lot more important, I thought, than proper etiquette. I didn't need to hear Mrs. Baldwin's stories, having heard them many times before. She'd been a real estate broker in D.C. and made a lot of money selling homes to cabinet officers and senators. She'd even known Franklin Roosevelt, but made it clear that she'd never voted for him.

Later that evening when the pace of work in the hot kitchen slowed down, I went back into the coolness of the dining room. Jennifer was still sitting at Mrs. Baldwin's table looking like she'd never gotten up.

"My goodness, you have found me quite a waitress. And I guess you like her, too."

I smiled, wondering how much Jennifer had told her. "Yes, I do."

"This is going to be a fun summer. I love romance," said Mrs. Baldwin, gesturing for me to sit down, which of course I didn't. It was one thing for Jennifer to sit with her. She was young and just a college waitress, who didn't know better. But for me to do it would have been different, something which would have thrown everything that Dad had taught me right in his face and I couldn't do that. At that time in the hotel business the guests expected and demanded formality. Dad had learned strict hotel protocol as a bellhop back in 1930 and rigorously enforced it throughout the hotel.

Apparently oblivious to the fact that I hadn't sat down, Mrs. Baldwin continued as if giving a college lecture. "I met Archibald back in college when I was twenty, but his parents wouldn't allow us to marry. I wasn't good enough, didn't come from a family with money."

I smiled thinking about a recent story I'd heard about a summer resident's daughter breaking off an engagement with a local boy. Her mother had referred to him as a "rustic." Some things don't change, I thought.

Mrs. Baldwin went on, "He married someone else, had children, went on with his life. I became a career gal, never married, and didn't need anyone's money. But Archibald's wife died and, forty years to the date of his first proposal, he proposed again. You never know how things are going to turn out."

Mrs. Baldwin paused, and then looked at me. "Oh my, I'm talking too much. I hope I'm not boring you. It's a curse of being old. Old people talk way too much, you know."

I reached over and did something I had never done with any guest—I put my hand over her hand. "Go on."

I sensed that Jennifer had told Mrs. Baldwin about the afternoon and how we were going to be together only for the summer. Maybe Jennifer had felt my disappointment and discussed it with her new friend. Maybe Mrs. Baldwin had offered her story as a glimmer of hope for me. Regardless, I was beginning to see Mrs. Baldwin as a real friend. And whatever ultimately came to pass with Jennifer and me, at least my summer wasn't going to be so lonely. There were going to be a lot of afternoons on the beach. I'd worry about fall later.

CHAPTER 6

DEAD LOBSTERS AT THE CHURCH

For the next two weeks I didn't take any more afternoons off. It was now mid-July, the season was at its height, and Dad seemed to always be walking through the kitchen. So Jennifer and I limited our bike riding to late afternoons, that time after the luncheon sandwiches had been made and the prep work for dinner was stuffed into the ovens. But I wanted more time with her. Every time the dishwashers' radio played Afternoon Delight during lunch, I'd glance out one of the greasy kitchen windows and wonder how long it would be till Jennifer returned from her bicycle training.

One morning during breakfast, I stepped outside for a break. It had been the kind of breakfast where four sheets of bacon hadn't been enough. The cement of the loading dock was hot. It could fry the extra pan of bacon that I had just put into the oven.

A seeming smell of the sea hung in the air; not fresh salt air, but the stench of rotten sea grass. I noticed a wooden crate hanging over the end of the loading dock, looking like it could fall off at any moment and the back end of a delivery truck vanishing in the dust down the rutted road. I pulled the crate off the edge and opened it. Inside, lobsters were lying motionless in what had become their coffin. The ice surrounding them had melted, causing them to cook a slow, oozing death and the little sacks in the middle of their backs to open, spilling poison.

I remembered Dario inspecting lobsters. If they weren't moving, he'd throw them into the garbage. If they moved slowly, like they were close to dying, he'd take a cleaver and chop their heads off. "Lobster must go sleep, hot water or quick, no time for poison," he would say.

So much for tonight's special, I thought. The bacon was waiting inside and so were waitresses with other orders. I had to get back to work. I'd deal with the dead lobsters later, as the crate was too heavy to throw into the trash without help.

Sometime later, after running out of blueberries for the pancakes and hollandaise for the eggs Benedict, I collapsed into what had been Dario's old cane chair in the chef's office. Soon Jennifer came in with a couple of cold beers, her hair wild from riding the twenty miles to Petoskey and back. I normally wouldn't drink that early, but it was one of those days.

"Let's go to the beach," she said, "dive down to the bottom of the lake, and stay there till we cool off."

Bleary-eyed and exhausted, I'd had enough. I had to get out of the steam room that served as a kitchen. Lunch would work out okay without me, and if it didn't, too bad. I called one of my cooks over and told him to handle lunch. If the cook couldn't find cranberry sauce for a turkey sandwich, I didn't care. I fixed us a couple of sandwiches, and we were out the door.

Sometime during the afternoon, between naps in the hot sun and dives toward the lake bottom to see who could go the deepest, I remembered the lobsters. I wondered if the cook would bother to throw them into the garbage hopper or if he'd just leave them there. It didn't matter. They were dead anyway, and I had Jennifer on my mind.

When I returned to the kitchen from my delicious afternoon, I noticed that the lobsters were gone. The cook said he'd gotten rid of them. That was good enough for me. I pulled out roasting pans and prepared to cook duck, my replacement special for the lobsters.

An hour later as the ducks were beginning to take on the orange scent of Grand Marnier, Dad entered the kitchen.

"Someone from a church on Barnesville Road just called to thank me for a lobster dinner. What the hell does that mean?"

My eyes widened as I looked around at my second cook.

He was silent, his eyes darting around as if he'd committed some terrible crime. He confessed, "I took them lobsters to my church—figured they were dead. A fancy place like this wouldn't serve them, but they're still good, ain't they? I'll pay you for them."

There wasn't time to explain. Dad dialed the church and stood there in the kitchen listening to the ringing of the unanswered phone, looking at the ceiling as if he was praying, but that couldn't have been the case. Probably they were all outside enjoying their lobsters, the dead, poison ones that would make them all very, very sick.

Dad drove the winding roads through the countryside at the speed of a racing ambulance, both of us hoping that we wouldn't be calling one. We sped right up onto the church lawn next to a bonfire and big metal pots. As we leapt from Dad's Cadillac we saw that the lobsters hadn't been served yet. Thank God.

We explained the problem to the hungry church folks, the faces of the children dropping as they realized that they weren't going to have a lobster dinner after all. They looked poor, like they didn't have much, and this would have been a special treat. Dad and the pastor walked over to the church where Dad used the phone to call the hotel and give orders to have a pile of steaks sent over immediately.

In the car on the way home, Dad didn't say anything. He glanced at me from time to time, looking at me like I was some kind of family retainer, someone he couldn't rely on to do a man's work. If I had stayed in the kitchen and worked lunch like I was supposed to, this wouldn't have happened.

I sat there trying to rationalize my actions in my mind. I was tired and overworked and needed an afternoon on the beach with Jennifer. Wasn't he ever young with such needs? Besides, the guests all loved my cooking. I was doing a hell of a job. Didn't he appreciate it?

Apparently not, as he continued to glare at me in the same way he once looked at Gordy, who managed to mangle everything he touched.

Gordy was the slow, late-in-life child of an older couple who had been guests at the hotel when Dad first bought it. When I was in college they'd died, and Gordy, in his late thirties, had been sent away to a "school." In one of his more gracious moments, Dad had offered to be responsible for Gordy during his usual one-month vacation at the hotel, so the school allowed him to continue coming.

That first summer Gordy arrived wearing an all-white uniform and proclaiming to me and everyone else at the airport that he had come to bus tables at the Colonial Inn. Dad didn't quite know what to do with him. He wasn't an employee, but he wasn't a regular guest either. He couldn't simply be left on his own for a month, so Dad decided to let him work in the dining room. At least there he could be watched and hopefully not get in too much trouble.

But soon Dad realized that he'd made a horrible mistake. Gordy, who wanted to work three meals a day, didn't seem to be able to do anything right. Dad was stuck too, because all the guests knew Gordy's situation and felt sorry for him, so there was no way Dad could send him back. And this went on for some years, with Dad liking it less each summer.

A guest who'd been burned when Gordy spilled hot coffee on his trousers told Dad that Gordy should be institutionalized. Dad turned to him and said, "He is, you know."

Now Dad was giving me the same look that he used to give Gordy when he would drop a tray of dishes or spill something.

Looking back, I can understand his frustration with me. I can see that Dad just didn't want to deal with things and have to fix my mistakes. He wanted to put on his red sport coat and entertain his guests on the front porch. Or maybe he was a bit jealous. Maybe he didn't like being the heavy old guy; maybe he wished he was young and had spent the afternoon on the beach.

CHAPTER 7

THE WAITRESS DORM HAS VALUE OTHER THAN SEX

July matured into August and, with its passing, the newness of the summer ebbed away. After a month of cooking three meals a day, seven days a week, I was getting tired. But I was now considering the little cubicle behind the kitchen storeroom surrounded by chicken-wire to be my office and not Dario's.

Outside the office windows I had been noticing that the leaves of the maples were drying silver. Fall with its inevitable insecurity was coming. I was getting worried. Where was my life going? Was Dad still thinking of selling? He hadn't mentioned anything about the future. I was too scared to talk to him about becoming the manager or eventually buying the hotel on an installment sale. Looking back, I'm still not sure if I could have done anything differently, the situation was so volatile. I had pushed Dad into postponing his retirement; anything more might have been too much. He would have called the developer.

Sneaking out of lunch early for bike rides with Jennifer wasn't enough to keep me from worrying. I wanted to reach out and grab what was left of summer, taste it, and hold on to it. I didn't want Jennifer to go, leaving me alone to face my future. I wanted again to see the sword grasses of Wilderness Beach shivering against the dunes.

Somehow, I thought if I could get Jennifer back there she might stay, go to school in Michigan, and be near me. But I could never find the time to return with her there. The hours I had between lunch and dinner just weren't enough.

By now Jennifer was spending more time with Mrs. Baldwin than me. She and Mrs. Baldwin would sit on the front porch near the big oak tree before dinner and visit like school girls who had been friends their whole lives. Employees weren't allowed to fraternize with guests, but Dad said nothing, because it was Mrs. Baldwin. Walking by, I would hear them discussing the plots and themes of books I'd read long ago but forgotten. It was like she was prepping Jennifer for some big test.

Late one moonless night while Jennifer and I were lying on the dock, our clothes strewn to the side, a couple of empty bottles of Bordeaux bobbing in the water, she whispered, "Mrs. Baldwin's been the best thing in my life. I'll always remember you for it."

I wished that Jennifer had said that I was the best thing in her life, but she hadn't. I looked out at the dark water, fixing on the bobbing bottles, feeling her drifting away, feeling empty. I wanted to talk, make plans, discuss the future, but swallowing, I merely said, "It's been a great summer."

I lay there wondering what I was going to do when she went back to school, facing another winter alone at the hotel. I wasn't a college student, with bright eyes and excitement for the world like Jennifer. I had turned twenty-eight a few days earlier. My life was real. My cooking wasn't a pretend summer job. Dad would be turning sixty-six in the fall. We hadn't talked much lately, but I knew he was still thinking of selling.

I had to make something happen. The wrecking ball wasn't far away. Dad was paying me twenty thousand dollars for the summer—good money, more than I had made at the firm. But even accumulated over years it wouldn't have been enough to buy the hotel. In a few weeks the quality of my duck wouldn't matter. I'd have to listen to Dad bitch that he should have sold.

I'd hear about the old man with a successful hot dog stand who sent his son to college, and how the kid came home with new ideas and ruined his father's business. Dad would then go on about how Allen Silverstein had ruined his father's florist shops back in Milwaukee. He'd been telling those stories since I was a kid riding in his cigarette haze in the back seat of his Cadillac.

Dad had stopped bragging to the guests about my degrees, as he'd done for so many summers. He hadn't said it, but I felt that he thought I was a failure for not sticking with my legal career. I was afraid that he was embarrassed—he'd boasted that I'd be a big time lawyer, not a cook. Looking back, I think that I was projecting my own feelings onto his. I was the one who was embarrassed, not him. The hot dog stand story was a defense mechanism for Dad's own feeling of inadequacy. He was saying that it was possible to be successful without a college degree.

A few days later I slipped into the dim cocktail lounge for a drink after the kitchen closed. I was tired and felt that I could melt into the seclusion of the piano music. Jennifer had gone out to the movies with Mrs. Baldwin, so I sat at the end of the bar alone. I had my martin down to where the olives were out of the gin when Allen sat next to me.

"I've been talking to your dad. You've got problems," he said. "He's still thinking of selling. That's a lot of money he turned down."

I nodded, gulping down the rest of my martin.

"So this developer would tear the whole place down and build condos everywhere?"

"Yeah," I said without looking up.

"You got a lot of land here—old dormitories, cottages, and extra parking. Why don't you find a developer who would build on just part of it? Maybe get enough money so that your dad would feel secure enough to sell you the hotel."

Setting my drink down, I looked over at him thinking I was lucky to have a big-time guy like Allen advising me. "You've got something. Those old buildings occupy half our land."

"You could have a nice condominium project without tearing down the hotel. Any idea on how much a unit your dad was going to get for the raw land?"

I smiled as I did some quick mental math. "About twenty thousand."

"That's lousy. Land like this should be forty, especially with the hotel still here adding to the value. You could get your dad the same money and keep the hotel. Maybe he'd give you a cheap deal, finance it."

I thought about it. It made sense. I had already discovered that, as a lawyer in Michigan, I could easily pick up a broker's license and make a lot of money selling the units. Hadn't Mrs. Baldwin made a fortune selling real estate? Maybe I could do the same. It'd be natural to sell them out of the hotel. Dad's real estate developer hadn't just been greedy; he'd been dumb, not seeing the value the hotel would add to the project.

I ordered another martin and a scotch for Allen, thinking about Dad retiring with plenty of money and me ending up with the hotel. Halfway through my drink, crunching the ice, reality hit. At my young age, it was doubtful I could sell the concept to a developer. I set my drink down and stared across the room. "I don't know if I can do it."

"It's a question of confidence. If you believe in the idea, that's most of the battle. My dad used to say, 'Your toughest sale is yourself. Make that sale and the others will come.'"

I chewed more ice, thinking easier said than done. Allen went on. "Notice that everyone around here thinks that I'm important?"

"Yeah."

"Well, that's because I've made them believe that I am."

"You've got the success to back you up. I don't."

Allen set his drink down and fixed me with a gaze. "Tim." He cleared his throat. "I'm not really a pharmaceutical representative. I'm only a clothing salesman."

I looked into his eyes. I couldn't believe what he was saying. Was he testing me? Did he want to see if I was buying his salesmanship crap?

"You shitting me? That's the biggest pile of crap I've ever heard."

"I'm sorry to say, it's true. When my dad's flower shops failed just before he died, I lost my drive. I had no confidence left. I floated around for years until a friend gave me a job selling clothes. That's why you haven't seen me in years. It's taken time to get my life back on track, to believe in myself. It hasn't been easy to come back to the place where everyone knew my dad."

I thought about Dad's hot dog stand story. Was Dad right? Did Allen ruin the flower shops? I was afraid to ask. So I said, "Why all the lies?"

Allen hung his head. I could see the bald spot on the back of his curly hair.

"When I first got here, I didn't plan to lie. It just happened. I felt like my dad was still here. I didn't want his friends to think that I had become only a clothing salesman. I could never face my father and I guess I couldn't face his friends."

I thought about the wealthy resorters I'd seen Allen hobnobbing with. In Harbor Springs, there's pressure to be somebody. And if a person wants to be somebody, he has to have the right kind of friends.

Allen would put on his oxford button down, tie his crew neck sweater around his shoulders, take his scotch, and stroll the curvy sidewalk under the big oaks in front of the waterfront cottages, one porch party after another. He seemed to have met everybody. This was an amazing feat since he wasn't from the association and, although it was never discussed, I assumed he was Jewish, which could have been a real black mark against him. But years ago his mother had somehow talked her way into getting him into the children's summer program. Allen had become an excellent tennis player, and he'd been generous at sharing his talents with the other children, which earned him a lot of friends. Hence he had grown up with many of these people and now he, too, had a childhood connection with them.

Allen and I sat in the shadows at the end of the bar listening to the piano music for a few minutes. Then he went on, just as if he hadn't made the confession of his life. "You can find a developer, make him feel right about the deal, appreciate what you have here."

Sitting there, trying to ingest the wisdom of his advice, I began to reason that if Allen had been able to pull off his charade, maybe I could sell the partial condo plan to a developer. But I worried that word would get back to Dad that I was trying to find a developer, meddling in his affairs. That might anger him to the point of selling.

I grasped his hand. "I'll do it, but how?"

"I'll approach a few people for you. Give me a few days."

I got up and shook Allen's hand, worrying that my future was now in the hands of a failed flower-shop-operator-turned-clothing-salesman who faked being wealthy and talked about raw land cost like he was a developer. But I had nowhere else to turn and, frankly, I believed in him. It seems Allen was a good salesman after all.

A couple of days later, Allen had a potential developer waiting for me in the lounge after dinner. Walter Chambliss had a big cottage near the hotel where his family had summered for generations. When Allen had met him at a porch party, he'd liked the idea of using the hotel to promote the condominiums.

When I walked into the lounge that night I saw Allen sitting near the piano with a tall heavy fellow leaning toward him listening. This guy looked like the kind of person who went through doors first, the kind of guy who would have it his way. He probably drove a station wagon with wood paneling, played tennis at ten, golf at one, and poured his martins on his porch at six.

As I pulled up a chair and introduced myself, I wondered why a socially connected person like him would even want to develop condominiums in a place where his family and their friends had been summering for over a hundred years. But then I thought, even rich folks could always use a few extra bucks. Maybe their winter home in Palm

Beach needed new landscaping. So I got right to the point.

"The hotel would add to the development potential of condominiums here, don't you think?"

For an hour we discussed acres, units per square foot, and construction cost. Then Walt pulled out a pen and, on a cocktail napkin, began sketching where condominiums could be built around the existing hotel.

"That's perfect!" I said. "We'll have a limited supply, which will create a unique atmosphere around our existing hotel."

Walt stood. "Let's talk tomorrow morning," he said.

He turned and moved toward another table with empty glasses all over it, where a group of his friends were working hard on their cocktails, not offering to shake hands. But I didn't care. I had a deal in the works that could get me the hotel, or so I thought.

The next morning after cooking breakfast, I showered quickly. Smelling like scrambled eggs and bacon just wouldn't put forth the businesslike image I was trying to convey. I grabbed a survey of the hotel grounds, hopped onto my bike, and headed down Beach Drive, past white docks where children were beginning to raise colorful sails on square-nosed prams and paddle out into the flatness of Little Traverse Bay, where the wind would soon rise.

I rode past the Wequetonsing association green, just up from its pier, where the morning croquet games were beginning. The warm summer sun was in my face but, squinting a bit, I could see the members dressed all in white, wearing wide-brimmed hats. They were milling about on the fresh-cut Bermuda grass. A few weeks later, after Labor Day, if any of them lingered, they wouldn't be wearing white. That just wouldn't be proper.

I imagined that they were discussing the stock market or their upcoming tennis or golf. I so wanted to be rich, to be part of that life and hoped that maybe the condominium project would move me toward that goal. Then I passed a woman with long straight blonde hair in her mid fifties with big bubble sunglasses. That wasn't surprising because older women in Weque and the Point think that they defy age by continuing to wear their school-girl hair styles well into later life. Regardless, their faces are portraits of the wealth from which they come. She was carrying a floppy tennis bag with the embroidered words "bring back Penn Dixie." I didn't have to ask what it meant; that would have been a sure sign that I didn't belong.

Penn Dixie had been the name of an obnoxious cement plant across Little Traverse Bay that had polluted the air of Northern Michigan for over a half a century until it had been torn down some years earlier. Now there was talk of building a giant real estate development on its former grounds. My neighbors made it clear that they despised the idea of new money with potentially undesirable people coming into their area so much that they would rather have the cement plant back. I realized that money made from real estate, especially in their own back yard from the boy who'd made their Caesar salads, would never cut it. But I didn't care.

The Chambliss home was a three-storied, Victorian monster built by Walt's great grandfather. It didn't look like the kind of place that would be occupied by someone who had to stoop to real estate. But then Dad always said you had to add new money to old money to keep it old.

I remembered that one of Walt's neighbors had told me that she hadn't cared for him because she'd heard that his money had come from real estate, implying that money earned in that way was somehow inferior. I guessed that it just didn't conform to the old families' manner of accumulating wealth, which was usually through something substantial like manufacturing.

I parked my bike and walked up the front steps to the porch, where a Filipino houseman greeted me. He showed me to a wicker chair that looked like it was built for an NFL running back, except that it was white and had pink and blue chintz cushions. I started to sit, but then decided it would be better to remain standing.

A few minutes later, the wide screen door to the front of the house creaked as Walt came out carrying a mug of steaming coffee. He looked like he needed it, his face betraying last night's drinking. Walt waved his hand toward the big chair next to me, motioning me to sit, which I did. Then the Filipino houseboy asked if I'd like something to drink. I asked for a Diet Coke with a wedge of lime and leaned back, savoring my newfound connection with wealth. Looking out at the bay through a leafy willow tree that looked like it came from a Gainsborough painting, I thought again about how nice it would be to be rich.

Walt made himself comfortable on the sofa across from me and, after a few pleasantries, asked to see the survey which I'd brought—a good start, I thought, but still I worried that our conversation the previous night may have been cocktail driven and not substantive.

As I unrolled the survey onto the coffee table in front of me, Walt leaned over to examine it and asked, "We can get about twenty-five units here?"

"Yes."

"Allen says that you need about forty thousand a unit?"

I looked out at the lake, not wanting to show weakness. I wondered what he was thinking; that I was just a dumb kid or that this proposition had merit? He was going to be in cool pine-scented breezes playing golf with millionaires this afternoon; I was going to be in a hot greasy kitchen teaching dishwashers how to roast prime rib. "Yeah, that's right," I answered in as strong a voice as I could muster, hoping that I wasn't conveying an undertone of anxiety.

"That'd be a million dollars."

Jeez, a million bucks. I hadn't thought of it like that. I took a sip of my Diet Coke, tasting the sharpness of the lime and hearing the clinking of ice cubes as my hand trembled. Easy now, I told myself. Don't act too excited. Let it rest.

Trying to convey confidence that I was far from feeling, I nodded, took a deep breath, and plunged ahead. "I'd also like to be your exclusive sales agent and sell the units right from the hotel. It'd add a sense of exclusivity that buyers couldn't just go to a local realtor. I believe that'd increase the perceived value."

I sat there on Walt's porch noticing that it had quite a lean toward the lake. When someone's got money it's okay to have things a bit ramshackle.

"Okay, you talk to your dad. My attorney will call you." Walt stood. It was a done deal.

I couldn't believe that I was going to get Dad almost as much money as the entire hotel would have brought last December.

Before I could stand, Walt stepped forward and loomed over me. "One last thing, and it could kill the deal. My name can never be connected with the deal. I've got a local front-man who'll handle things and take the heat."

I stood and shook Walt's hand. "No problem." I knew that I could keep his name secret. I'd had a lot of experience in the hotel keeping my mouth closed around the resort community. More than a few marriages would have been injured if I'd not learned the art of discretion. I wasn't worried about killing the deal; I was worried about Dad's reaction to it.

I rode back to the hotel, noticing that the wind had begun to kick up. There were now small waves on the lake, where children raced their tiny boats, their striped sails zigzagging about. Later, when the wind got stronger, the big boats would be out filling the bay, but for now it was only the children. It was a peaceful scene, but counter to my excited state of mind. I had to get to the hotel. I had to talk to Dad.

I barged into his dingy old office and smelled the stale cigarettes. "Dad, I've got deal for you . . ."

After I finished explaining the details, Dad leaned back in his chair, squinting at me. "So you put this together, eh? You sure he'll really pay that much?"

Grateful that he didn't ask why I was out looking for a developer or how I found Walter, I said, "I think so."

Then, remembering Allen's words about self-confidence, I decided that I might as well see where I really stood.

"How about selling me the hotel if he does? With this deal, would you reduce the price and sell it to me on terms?"

Dad lit up a Camel, blowing more smoke into the already saturated air. "Let's stick to this condo deal and not get sidetracked."

My ears rang as I stood before him, stunned. Didn't he realize that the whole point of this new deal was for me to get the hotel? His tepid reaction threw me. I thought that maybe I hadn't been clear, but in my mind I was on track. So I raced full-steam ahead.

"With a million cash from the land sold for the condos, you wouldn't have to worry so much about me being able to keep up the payments on the hotel itself. And I'll be able to get the down payment from the commissions from selling the units."

Dad blew a smoke ring and followed its progress toward the window.

"My grandfather, the best hunter in the mountains of Tennessee, used to say, 'We'll talk about cutting up the meat after we shoot the bear.'"

I stood there wondering why Dad wouldn't say yes. I got him a better deal; he'd been willing to sell anyway. Why not sell to me? I couldn't understand it. I walked out and closed the door, figuring that arguing would have been pointless. At least I'd be making tremendous real estate commissions. Any sale of the hotel would be put off.

At the time, I'd thought of only the monetary part of the deal. I hadn't realized that winning the hotel wasn't an end in itself; it was a means to manhood and respect from Dad. I hadn't learned yet how to communicate with him, to make him take me seriously. That would come much later after a lot of growing and pain.

That night, in the shadows of the tall cedars lining the back of the kitchen, Jennifer snuck up the back stairs to my attic-kitchen apartment as she had been doing all summer. She was the first girl I had actually lived with and I wasn't sure how Mother would handle it, so we just kept it quiet. When we cuddled up on Dario's old twin bed, with the springs jabbing at my side, I was about to tell her about the big meeting and my bright future.

But before I could begin, she squeezed my hand and said, "I've got big news. Mrs. Baldwin has arranged for me to transfer this September to her alma mater, Bryn Mawr, in New York. She's well connected and knows publishers and editors. With her help I'll be a writer someday."

I lay there in the dark, speechless, feeling her body next to mine and my heart beating against hers. I'd known from our first afternoon on the beach that Jennifer would be leaving in September. She'd made that clear. But I'd still hoped that she'd transfer to some college in Michigan, the summer had gone so wonderfully. I'd brought it up a number of times, only to be answered by a big smile and a gaze off into the distance. Now I knew why. She had her big plans, too. I knew that Mrs. Baldwin could make Jennifer's life a success. New York and Colorado were both far away. Jennifer had new places to go, new people to meet, and new things to do. I had to let her go.

I realized I'd miss her mostly because I'd be alone again, not because I loved her—not like I had loved my first girlfriend back in college. We'd never had any of that making-plans that couples do when they're falling in love. Thinking back, I remembered that we never spent any time talking about the future. We only talked about what was going on that day or maybe the next week.

I fell asleep thinking of my own big plans. Even if Dad didn't sell me the hotel, I'd still earn hefty commissions and learn about real estate development. Maybe Jennifer was going to be a writer, but I was going to get rich, maybe have my own houseboy someday, just like Walt Chambliss did. That seemed like a good idea.

CHAPTER 8

MISERY ON THE DOCK

A few weeks later the hotel closed for the season and with it another part of my life ended. Jennifer stayed a couple of extra days so that we could enjoy some of the things we had missed during the summer. We spent our last magic hours riding the few country roads we hadn't explored and watching sunsets on beaches we had missed. We rolled in the sand without any cares. There was no work to return to, no hot kitchen, only the pleasures of three special days.

On her last evening we rode our bikes on the winding road through the dark trees back to Wilderness Beach. It had been our only trip back there since that beginning afternoon when the summer was new and green, and it would be our last.

We lit a fire, talked, roasted hot dogs, and drank red wine till the evening chill forced us under our blankets. I was glad for the wine and gulped it down because we'd made a pact not to talk about the future, but rather to pretend that the summer was still ahead. The wine made that easier to do. It seemed better that way, not to let emotions get in the way. We'd had a summer without them or without planning for the future, so why not our final night?

I awoke early and looked at Jennifer lying next to me in the cold September sand. During the night we must have kicked the blanket out from underneath us. Over her tangled hair, out to the east above the scrub pine to where the night was beginning to lift, I could see a ribbon of clear sky which held the new sun.

Jennifer, who must have also been looking at the sun, reached up and kissed me. "We made it come up," she said.

Putting my arms around her, I noticed the beginning of light reflecting on the lake still engulfed in blackness. The day was coming. Nothing could be done to hold it back, and with it, Jennifer was leaving.

We sprang apart and ran into the frigid water of Lake Michigan to rid ourselves of gritty sand. Soon we scampered out of the lake, shivering as we waited for the frail sun to dry us. In the damp morning dew, we dressed, ate some granola bars, and doused the remaining embers of last night's fire. As we rolled up our blankets, I looked over at Jennifer and noticed lake water dripping down her long hair.

"I'll miss you. Could you come back from New York and meet me in Ann Arbor for a football game?"

I suppressed an urge to tell her that I loved her and that I was going to be so damn lonely without her. I didn't think it would do any good and wasn't sure if I really loved her. So instead I added, "I don't want this to be the end."

I stood there searching her face for some sign that I had meant something, but there was none. She said nothing in reply, just looked at me with those eyes that said I want adventure, the same eyes that had infatuated me back in early July. Then silently we mounted our bikes for the ride back to Harbor Springs.

On the long way back home through the winding tunnel of trees already hinting of color, we said little. There was nothing more to say. It had all been said or didn't need to be said. The summer traffic was gone. Only a few cars and a pickup truck with a windsurfer in its bed passed us. With no wind to stir the trees, I could hear the wheels of our bikes kicking out the occasional bits of gravel.

Back at the hotel Jennifer's parents would be waiting to take her home, back to Colorado, then pack her off to New York, another faraway place. I wondered what it would be like to meet the parents of the girl I had been with all summer. I wondered if they would approve of me. But then I realized that it didn't matter. We'd shake hands, visit for ten or fifteen minutes, and they'd be gone.

That night I sat alone on the cold planks of the hotel dock with a bottle of Tanqueray next to me and a martin in my right hand. Most of the surrounding cottages were now unlit, their residents gone till next June, making it much darker than even the moonless nights during the summer that I had spent discussing my future on the dock with Jennifer. I lifted my eyes and gazed out into the darkness as I tried to contemplate what her life would be like. She'd be meeting people in the literary world, going to Broadway shows, and meeting young men, future writers. I rattled the ice in the bottom of my glass and drank down the gin, telling myself it didn't matter. She was gone, and I welcomed the slight burning in my throat.

I poured another drink and gulped it. Then it occurred to me that except for the night at the bar with Allen, I hadn't had a martin all summer, just wine. Now suddenly I drifted back to the hard stuff. But it was worth it; the ensuring warmth numbed me and brought at least temporary relief from my situation—loneliness.

Later that night when the effect of the alcohol wore off, I awoke in Dario's old bed and began tossing about, unable to sleep without Jennifer next to me. The lumps in the mattress were now bothering my back. Strangely, I hadn't been aware of them all summer.

The next morning, I awoke early, and with nothing else to do, rode my bike back to our beach. I thought that somehow being there would make me feel closer to her. It seemed like the thing to do. Reminiscing might make some of the pain go away.

A few moments later, without even considering breakfast, I was on M119 racing my bike toward Wilderness. As I rode, I looked down the steep sandy bluff to the blue waters of Lake Michigan. What a funny thing time is, I thought. Once something is in the past, it's always in the past. Thousands of years ago Lake Michigan was hundreds of feet higher, its waters lapped at the very bluff I was now riding on. And yesterday Jennifer was riding with me. In the scheme of things, both were irretrievably gone.

I felt that I was in a time warp between the past with Jennifer and the future where I was going to be rich. I vowed that I wouldn't dwell on Jennifer. I would walk the beach and take stock of my life, looking not to the dead past, but to the future.

I picked up my speed, closing the gaps between the trees. Fast felt good as if I could out race my doubts.

An hour later I leaned my bike against the white bark of a birch tree and began walking on the beach, dragging my feet in the warm sand. I had made it through a hot, greasy summer of commercial cooking. Unlike the chefs on gourmet television shows, after cooking two hundred dinners nightly I didn't even want to see food, let alone eat it. I just wanted to get drunk. I could finally understand why Dario and Benny drank so much; an occupational hazard. I was glad that I had Jennifer that summer. Without her to share my thoughts, I would have done a lot more drinking.

I could see lighthouses shimmering forty miles out in the lake. Jennifer was gone, but my life was moving forward. That's where I needed to look, not behind me. There'd always be next summer and perhaps another Jennifer. That's what I told myself. But I also knew that the older I got, the harder it would be to find a girl with adventure in her eyes, who saw life and love as new.

On one of the last mornings of September I walked down the beach sidewalk to the Chambliss cottage. The docks that had floated peacefully all summer while bare-footed children padded about them were now stacked on the shore, and the colorful sailing prams that had plied the bay had been put away in dark garages for the winter. The bay no longer welcomed children in red life vests, its regattas over. As I turned to climb the tall steps to Walt's front porch, I heard waves crashing against the boulders on his beach.

At the top of the stairs, Walt was waiting with what looked to me a half-hearted smile to introduce me to Joe, a bald-headed fellow in a red-checkered shirt. We shook hands and walked onto the porch, surrounded by clear plastic curtains that shielded us from the chill lake wind and made me feel a bit warmer. Walt motioned for us to sit on floral-cushioned chairs around a coffee table, where a survey of the hotel had been spread. On it someone had penciled in where the condominiums were to be built. Walt grinned.

"What do you think of our site plan?"

So, I thought, a survey that shows potential buildings must be called a site plan. I vowed not to let on that I didn't know that. I bent over the survey and studied it for a few minutes, noting the proposed property split and the number of units, twenty-five. "Yeah, I like it."

Just then Walt's Filipino houseboy brought a pot of coffee and poured a cup for Walt and Joe. Watching Joe meticulously add sugar and cream to his coffee, then slowly stir the contents, I couldn't help but think that he'd probably had a lifetime of looking after details. A couple of minutes later the houseboy returned with a tall glass of ice with slice of lime and a can of Diet Coke for me. What an excellent fellow to have remembered what I drank! I was sure that I was one of Walt's least important visitors. I told myself that when I became rich, I would have to have someone like the Filipino attending to my needs.

I took a sip of my Coke. "I've heard we're going to have some trouble. There're a lot of people who want to stop our project."

Walt leaned back in his big wicker chair, trying to get a better look at a lone sailboat bouncing around on the bay. "We'll work it out. It's all a question of negotiation. You just got to know how to present things."

I felt the men's eyes on me. My gaze wandered to the bouncing sailboat as the Coke settled uncertainly on my stomach. "I guess so."

"Now, you've known from the beginning that we've got to get a change of zoning. All of our figures are based on that," said Walt.

"You also told me not to worry."

"I still believe the city made a mistake when they zoned Colonial Inn. They didn't mean to leave a large commercial property without practical uses," he said, pouring himself another cup of coffee.

"We're only asking to change the zoning to what it should have been for an existing hotel. Once that's done," he shrugged, like it was no big deal, "we're completely within the code, no variances or special privileges."

I nodded, but wasn't convinced. The code explicitly designated the Colonial Inn as general business, which excluded condominiums. That could be used to stop us. Why was Walt so confident? How did he know he could get his site plan approved?

Walt pointed to Joe, who had been slouching in the chair across from me, saying nothing. "Joe knows these guys and how they think and how to talk to them. We've worked together before. He's going to be in charge."

"All right," I said with a bravado that wasn't in my heart, looking down at the site plan, avoiding eye-contact with the chubby fellow sitting across from me who would now control the success of the project and my future.

"It's an old-boy network up here," said Joe.

"I understand," I answered, as if these sorts of dealings were a regular occurrence for me, too. But my eyes kept scouring the site plan as I tried, unsuccessfully, to picture the building that would rise there.

Without preamble Joe stood. That meant, I guessed, that the meeting was over. But then, staring down at me, he said, "I heard you can blow up. We can't have that. This is a delicate matter. You've got to sit in the back of the room during the meeting with your mouth shut. You and your dad aren't particularly popular here."

My head jerked up. "What do you mean? Who've you been talking to? I'll beat the shit out of them."

My cheeks burned, and I wondered for just a second if I had gone too far, but I wasn't going to let anybody talk to me like that. That was one of the reasons I had left the law firm. I wasn't going to be a pushed-around nobody.

Joe smiled and shook his head as if admonishing my schoolboy reaction. But at the time I wondered why he even brought it up. Dad and I, like anybody in the hotel business, had fired our share of folks. But this was a small town where grudges were harbored. Joe must have gotten a mouthful from someone. But we were doing a million dollar deal, and he was just doing his due diligence by checking us out. Still, I was pissed.

But Joe didn't answer me. He bent over and began rolling up the site plan.

I hesitated in my chair and felt beads of cold sweat forming on the back of my neck. Then I squared my shoulders and stood. "Tell me who's been bad-mouthing us."

Walt shot a swift warning glance, but I couldn't be sure if it was aimed at me or Joe. How important was I? I couldn't be sure. "Gentlemen, we're at a business meeting. You guys don't have to like each other, but you do have to work together."

I looked over at Walt, noted his steel eyes, thought about the money that I was going to make from this deal, and abruptly checked my tongue before I said what I was really thinking about Joe.

As I walked back home, feeling the stickiness that had formed in my armpits, I thought about zoning. What a mysterious subject it was, telling you what you could and couldn't do with your property. In all of law school, it'd only been touched on for an hour. Dad had always said, "If you want to build a forty-story pink pagoda, there are only two questions that should count: do you own the land and do you have enough money to pay for it?"

Other developments had been built in Harbor Springs, but not in our summer association locale. My neighbors didn't want condos built in their back yard, that was for sure. I could see why Walt wanted his name hidden. That was why he had someone like Joe.

Who the hell was Joe? Just a front man, seemingly. He'd probably taken all kinds of crap from Walt over the years. Maybe this was his chance to act like a big shot. I vowed that someday I'd kick him hard in the ass. But for now, I'd be nice. I'd suck up to him just the same as I did to a fussy old guest at the hotel.

But as I passed our dock, now barren planks stacked upon each other, my thoughts drifted from business to pleasurable memories. Snuggled in my sweater, I remembered the hot nights spent on it with Jennifer. But that now seemed long ago. Now I had other things to think about.

A month later, near October's end 1980, as the first snowflakes of the season drifted down into the night, I crowded into our little Norman Rockwell town hall with about a hundred other people. Long rows of lights blazed from the ceiling, making the dark paneled chamber look big-time and important. This was the night to present our zoning request. Inside people scrambled for seats while outside folks waiting to enter the narrow arched door could see their breath.

From my seat in the back of the room, by the overflowing coat rack, I looked around, listened, and tried to make sense out of the indistinguishable chatter surrounding me. With a feeling of uneasiness and a sense that most of the people were against us, I began to put words in their mouths that made my stomach churn. Dad, sitting next to me, started tapping his feet when a number of the people sitting around us nodded in agreement when a guy in a nylon jogging suit who looked like he had just moved to the area said, "We don't need any more condominiums."

I felt hurt and threatened. We had a good plan. What was the problem? My stomach churned as I felt the air of the overcrowded room thicken. Looking back, I realize that real estate developers have few friends. That's just the way it is when someone wants to change something for a species that most always fears and resists change.

As the room continued to fill, I noticed that Joe had pushed his chair up to the main table in the center of the room, where the board members sat. He was leaning back cracking jokes and laughing with them, as if they were already in his pocket. But that did little to reassure me.

Fifteen minutes later the wooden gavel came down with a clap and the meeting was called to order. Walt's architect argued that the present zoning of the hotel was hurriedly conceived and unfair. Then he did a thorough job of presenting the site plan, which he said required no variances.

The board deliberated for a while, then opened the discussion to the floor. A tall white-haired man immediately stood, cleared his throat, and said that the Colonial Inn had been deliberately zoned against condominiums, because it was in a sensitive area.

The room erupted into applause, then Dick Johnson, a neighbor who looked like Clark Gable fresh off a movie set, stood and turned right toward Dad and me, not Joe. He'd seen through the rouse. "My great-great grandfather began summering here in the 1880's. I don't want to see the area changed."

I'd heard that Mr. Johnson was a New York City investment banker and now I was starting to believe the rumors about his ruthless business activities. His hardened eyes pierced at us like we were some minor acquisition that he was going to gobble up.

My heart began pounding as I realized where the meeting was going—it wasn't good. In the front of the room I could see Joe shifting around uneasily on his chair. Things hadn't gone quite as he figured either. Good, he deserved it for leading me on. The light cast from the round frosted lights hanging from the ceiling started to look like one blob to me. Then the whole room blurred as I sat there on the edge of my hard chair, listening to Mr. Johnson and others hand out their vitriolic crap, in my estimation, for almost an hour. For the most part they were the very people whom I had grown up serving Caesar salads to. Now that they were sticking it to me, I wished that I hadn't spent so much time grinding up their anchovies.

Dad sat motionless, his face not revealing his thoughts, but I knew better. He was quietly sitting there intently surveying the people around him. It looked like he was making a mental list for some future use, and I knew how vengeful he could be. Did he blame me for all this? I was sure that he took it personally. It was his hotel, and having a bunch of inherited-money-people decide what he could do with it had to be unbearable. Looking back, I realize that Dad, with two years of college, mostly playing football, felt insecure around these people anyway. Their comments had to have rung his bell.

I sat fidgeting, all twisted up inside. I wanted to stand and tell my story. I wanted the folks in the audience to realize that most developers would have torn down the hotel and built three times as many condominiums. I wanted them to know that this was my chance to save the hotel, to keep it going. But I sat there silently, as I was told to do, and watched the board unanimously reject our request.

Before we left, I stared straight across the room at Joe. So much for his connections and persuasive ability, I thought. I wanted to tell him off, but figured I'd do it later. Now I just wanted to get out of the room before Dad or I exploded.

As Dad and I walked down the now icy steps of the city hall, I wondered how long it would be before he began talking of selling.

On the dark, moonless way home in Dad's old wood paneled Ford station wagon, we spoke not a word. Finally he whispered, "Pull over. I got to get some air."

We got out of the car and stood by a ditch filled with dying cattails. There were autumn-dead leaves all around us. Dad wiped the sweat off his forehead. I watched his breath form a haze in the icy night as he clutched his chest.

"Damn, I could have sold to a developer without a weasel clause for zoning. I'd have got less, but I wouldn't have had to go through this. I looked like an old fool, begging before a damn board. Thanks."

My greatest fears had been realized. I had blown the deal, hurt and humiliated my father, jeopardized his retirement, and made myself appear a fool in his eyes. Dad would probably sell now, and I had no other job. And now that the zoning was clearly not going to be changed, no other developer would want the hotel, making it worth a lot less.

"But, Dad, we didn't see this coming," I lied. I had seen it all the way, but refused to acknowledge the possibility, focusing only on my own dubious success and ambitions.

"Save it, just drive me home."

I didn't say a word as he lay down in the back of the station wagon, his breath labored. He was a heavy man and a smoker and, what with the unsettling events of the evening, I figured he might have a heart attack. The rest of the way home my eyes kept returning to the rear view mirror as I kept muttering, "How could I have been so stupid?"

Chapter 9

Hangovers can be slept off

I slept till noon the next morning. Why not? There was nothing to get up for. The hotel was closed. My dreams were ruined. Although I had never experienced it before, Dario's apartment was ideally suited for sleeping in late. The dark cedars encasing its windows blocked most of the morning sun, creating a cave-like feeling within its unpainted walls.

I got up, switched on the overhead light bulb dangling from the ceiling, and almost tripped over my Saint Bernard. I wondered what to do next. After fixing a cup of tea on the two-burner stove, I decided to call Walt, see where I should send his earnest money. I figured that I might as well get it over with. Dad always said, "There's no point in putting off anything unpleasant. If you wait, it just gets worse."

"I'm sorry," said the overly pleasant voice on the end of the line, "Mr. Chamblis isn't in."

I gave her my name and added, "I'm from the Colonial Inn. When will he be back?"

"Would you please repeat your name?"

Evidently my deal had been so small that Walt hadn't even bothered to mention it to his secretary.

"I'll call back."

"Well, don't bother calling this afternoon. Just give me your name again. He'll call you tomorrow."

Most likely Walt was playing golf with some resorter buddies down in Grosse Pointe. They were probably talking about the naive developer who had tried to build condos in their back yard. I thought about how I'd like to tell all the neighbors that he was behind the deal and get my revenge for what he'd done to Dad and me. But then I had a chilling thought; there would be no one to tell till next summer, and by then Dad probably would have sold out and I'd be gone.

Later that afternoon, when the frost had melted, I took Teddy out for a long walk. It was beginning to clear and even warm up. Someone said that it would hit sixty, one of the last warm days before the snow. The town looked like a picture postcard of a resort town, with distinct houses of brick, wood, and stucco and fieldstone surrounding the calm blue bay.

Walking along through the empty streets with the leaves meticulously piled at every corner, I couldn't blame my neighbors for not wanting condos. Had I been one of them, I would've felt the same. But it had been my big chance to get ahead, and I took it, for what it was worth.

A bit later when Teddy and I turned down a back road, I came across a pink house with robin-egg-blue shutters and a cedar shake roof surrounded by a split-rail fence. How odd, I thought. This wasn't in keeping with the simplicity of Harbor Springs. Any one of these characteristics might have fit, but certainly not all of them together. It was far too eclectic.

Teddy had started to roll about in an unusually large pile of leaves when someone called, "Timmy Brown, you still have a Saint Bernard."

I looked up and saw a pretty woman with a wide smile in her early forties with long dark hair curling loosely about her shoulders. She looked vaguely familiar, but I couldn't place her.

She walked down the brick path from the pink house to Teddy and began stroking his head just above his big white spot. "He can't be the same dog."

"I've only had him a year. It gets lonely up here in the winter. Got to have a dog."

"I hope I don't get lonely," she said, looking out across the piles of leaves heaped in front of her house.

"Do I know you?"

"You look so much like the Timmy that I knew. Those plaid Bermuda shorts were so cute on you. Do you still wear them?"

I smiled, befuddled, thinking that she must have been a guest at the hotel long ago. "Yeah, but it's fall now. They'd be a bit cold."

She laughed against the rising warm wind. "Well, I don't know, it's a question of style."

"We're not on an equal footing. You know about my dog and my shorts, but I don't know about you."

"I also know you're lonely, single, I presume, and bored."

"I never said anything about being bored."

"You didn't have to. Why else would you be out walking the dog every day all around this town?" She indicated a sign swinging on a post by her front door. "I've got an art gallery for my work. Come on in and have a look."

We headed up the path to her cottage, where wisps of smoke curled from the chimney. Inside, charred wood still smoldered in her fireplace. Her paintings covered every wall, a contrast to my apartment where neither Dario nor I had bothered to hang a single picture.

"You're a damn good artist. The best I've seen in Harbor Springs."

As Teddy plopped down by the door, she said, "Take a look at this one," moving to a painting of an old log bridge above a meandering brook. On the bridge a little boy in Bermuda shorts had his arm around the neck of a Saint Bernard.

The memories came rushing back. I turned to her, looking up and down. "You're Annie," I cried. "That's where we'd have picnics." I grasped the hands of a long-lost friend. "I remember when you painted it. You showed it to Mrs. Baldwin. She said you had talent and could be an artist. But you said art was just a hobby. But now look at you." I stood studying the bold strokes of color, the fine craftsmanship. "You've done it!"

She nodded at the painting. "Finally," She turned to me. "How about a cup of tea?"

We sat by the dying fire, where she told me her story. After business school at Michigan, she worked at Morgan Stanley's international finance department in New York, got transferred to Sydney, where she met her husband. Not a Crocodile Dundee, but a corporate accountant. The marriage lasted three years. She returned to New York.

"After a few years, they wanted to transfer me to Singapore. I couldn't do it, so I quit and began taking classes at the New York Art Institute. I dabbled in painting, sold some pieces down in the village, but it wasn't enough. I needed to come back to the place that inspired me—-Harbor Springs. I rented this house a couple of weeks ago and had it painted."

She talked about her art—where she was and where she was going with it. She, too, reminisced about how years ago Mrs. Baldwin had liked her art and had encouraged her to be an artist.

I told her that Mrs. Baldwin still spent her summers at the hotel and mentioned what she had done for Jennifer, launching her on her writing career.

Annie stared at her now-empty tea cup. "I wish I'd have listened to Mrs. Baldwin and just gone off to paint."

"Well, maybe you can tell her that next summer."

As shadows started to cast across the room, Annie looked up at me. "We've been talking all afternoon. I'm starved. How about dinner? I found a good pub over in Petoskey."

A few moments later we climbed into her old Ford truck with Teddy Bear snuggled between us on the bench seat. I stretched out with my arm hanging over the back of the crowded seat, careful not to touch Annie's shoulder. Still, though, I was conscious of her gentle fragrance.

"You like it?" she said, patting the dashboard. "I just bought it a few days ago. Plenty of room for my art supplies."

"I think Mrs. Baldwin would approve."

When we reached the pub it had begun to drizzle, the kind of damp weather Northern Michigan has just before it snows. Inside the little neighborhood place, we sat down on the cracked red vinyl benches and ordered a couple a cheeseburgers and beers.

When the beers arrived, Annie leaned back, wiped the frost off the window next to her, and stared outside. "I used to do investment banking in New York; now I'm an artist in Harbor Springs. I took care of you when you were a boy and now you're a man. Life changes."

I studied her profile, seeing still the young Annie I had known. "Maybe not so much."

Chapter 10

Something besides renting rooms and skiing

The next morning I sat in my tiny over-the-kitchen apartment, huddled next to the gas heater-fireplace. Dad had it installed a few years earlier when Dario's arthritis began bothering him on cool mornings.

Watching the blue flames curl around the end of a cement log, I remembered that Dad had always wanted Dario to stick around in the fall to see the color, but that never happened. Possibly that was why Dad had sprung for the faux fireplace. I smiled, picturing Dario huddled like me, watching this fake fire instead of fishing down in Florida.

The phone shrilled. I reached across a table to grab it as Teddy Bear, lying nearby on the floor, stretched his big paws and groaned into awakeness. It was Walt. "Hey, kid. Don't worry. It's not a big deal. We're not quitting; Joe's got a few more ideas."

"Really? We can go on? But no one at the meeting had been on our side. No one had even said anything nice about the project."

The bitter taste of that night returned—my failure and Dad's humiliation. But Walt seemed unconcerned.

"I'm going ahead. Our contract is binding until April first. We'll get the zoning changed."

"You're back to the zoning board again? You really think there's still a chance?"

"Grow up, kid. We're not going to take our toys and go home. Do you think I made my fortune by backing down just because things got rough?"

"Well, no, sir," I said, then chastising myself for calling him "sir."

"Joe still thinks that he can cut a deal."

"You're kidding."

"The board is just posturing. Joe will keep on things. He's a good guy. They like him."

"Really?" I didn't see him as all that likeable.

"Yeah, they do, and we'll get a change of zoning. It just takes time. I've done this before."

"That's hard to swallow from the way things went down at the meeting."

"I know," said Walt. "But we have a reasonable request and in the end we'll get it. The board knows what's fair. They were under a lot of pressure. They couldn't be seen as just giving in. It has to look like a compromise."

After I hung up, I wondered what he meant by compromise and was beginning to mistrust Walt. Our purchase agreement was based on twenty-five units, which would be allowable if the zoning was changed. I worried that Joe and Walt were going to cut the number of requested units in exchange for the change in zoning. What else could compromise mean? We had nothing else to give the zoning board in return. Walt and Joe probably had this planned all along. Why hadn't I seen it?

But I could see the chiseling now. Fewer units would mean less money for Dad. Walt would say that it wasn't his fault. He tried, but all he could get was eighteen or even sixteen units. He wouldn't be bound by the purchase contract because it called for twenty-five units. Walt would tell Dad that he was going to back out of the deal. He'd claim that he wouldn't be able to make any money with the reduced number of units. By then Dad would be so emotionally involved in the process that he'd accept a greatly reduced price. But he'd be so pissed that he would never sell me the hotel.

But even with big concessions I doubted that Walt and Joe would be able to make a deal. I didn't think they could get an outhouse past those board members. But the contract gave them the right to go forward till April first, so I went along.

At least Dad would be calmed by the possibility of the deal still happening. I could talk him into letting me operate the west building again this winter as a motel. An extra ten thousand dollars wouldn't hurt. Rubbing my hands together to create a little warmth, I thought about how nice it would be to move back to a king fireplace suite for the winter. Dario's apartment, even with the new-fangled-heater, wasn't suited for November winds.

I thought how fortunate I was to be able to prolong things till the next summer and next year, 1981. I figured that by the time the deal failed or Walt brought us a greatly reduced price, it would be spring and Dad would be too busy to think of selling.

That evening, Teddy and I walked to Annie's little apartment over her gallery. We had such a wonderful time at the pub in Petoskey that she'd asked me to dinner. Was this a date? I wasn't sure. But I found her enticing.

I climbed the stairs on the side of Annie's gallery. At the top, wearing paint-smeared jeans, cable sweater, and a warm smile, she welcomed me into her one-room apartment. Even smaller than Dario's apartment, it contained her kitchen, bed, and sofa all in one bright, pink room, with a round window overlooking the arbor to her gallery.

"I don't want to be tied down with things," she said. "I had a big home in New York. Now this is all I need. The gallery is where I'm going to spend my time."

I nodded, but was tempted to add that her reduced situation in life was similar to mine. We had a lot in common, poverty brought on by not following a traditional life.

"Hey, yeah, want to go to a party before dinner? Some of the locals are having an after-the-alligator affair up the street. Apparently they always do it when they're sure that last of the resorters have left. It sounds like fun and I want to be accepted here."

"Sure."

I looked down at the little alligator on my navy Lacoste shirt. It was emblematic of the summer snobbism that had been thrown in the face of the locals for years. It now loomed large to me as I wondered which world I belonged to.

Annie saw me staring down at it. "You can wear one of my painter shirts. I buy them extra large so I got room to move around when I paint."

I glanced at her and could see why she needed extra roomy shirts. She was lovely.

She walked over to a dresser and pulled out a faded blue work shirt with some globs of various colored paint smudges. "This'll do, but those Topsiders with no socks will give you away."

I agreed, remembering that the summer residents always wore them that way regardless of the season or temperature. It was a way of reminding everyone that they were summer-people, which was important to them. But that evening I had no other shoes so at least part of my identity would have to be revealed. Actually it was fitting because I wasn't really a resorter or a local.

Annie and I, with Teddy following, walked down her street a few blocks to the base of Judd hill where a bunch of people were having a street party. The beer was flowing and the stories were circulating. The object appeared to be who could come up with the best account of having been snubbed the previous summer. The winner seemed to be a lady who said that her eight-year-old-son had thought that he'd been invited to a birthday party at one of the resorters' homes, then when he'd actually shown up, the parents had called and told her to come get him, he hadn't been invited.

Regardless of the stories, which many might not have been true, unlike "hot dog night" at the association's summer program, I'd had a good time. At least for the moment I was able to put my problems aside as I was beginning to enjoy being with Annie.

When the party was over, Annie and I returned to her apartment and, with alcohol-enhanced appetites, consumed the linguini oregano that she'd prepared. Then we sat on her sofa, a respectable distance apart. She opened another bottle of merlot and poured a couple of glasses. Teddy sat at my feet, sniffing her shag carpet that must have been laid before Kennedy was president. I relaxed back into her sofa and looked across at Annie. There was something warm and familiar about her as well. I felt she would be my friend and I could confide in her, so after a while I opened up with what was on my mind.

"I've been duped by Walt Chambliss."

I told her about my desire to raise the money to buy the hotel and the ensuing zoning battles. She listened patiently and asked, "So you think in the spring the deal will fall apart?"

"Yes."

"Then you need something to do besides renting motel rooms, skiing, and reading duck recipes this winter. You need a way to start making some real money aside from Walt."

I sat up straight. "Of course. Damn good advice—something I should have thought of. But how?"

"Why not buy this building? The owner is a widow in poor health who has a lot of trouble taking care of it. I'll bet she'll sell cheap. And there are two other apartments besides mine and the gallery. The combined rent might be close to eighteen thousand. There's good money to be made as a landlord. My ex got rich doing it."

"God, that's more than I made in the law firm. But why are you telling me? Why don't you buy it?"

Annie got up and went over to the cabinet above the kitchen sink to get another bottle of Merlot. She opened it and turned toward me. "I don't know how long I'm going to stay here. When the time is right and I don't feel the inspiration anymore, I want to be able to just leave without any attachments."

She filled our glasses, sat next to me, and leaned forward. As the scent of her patchouli came to me, she fixed me with her dark brown eyes. "Get off your ass and buy it before somebody else does."

I sipped my Merlot and studied her as I tried to absorb where this could lead. Teddy was now lying down with his chin resting on his front paws and studying me, almost like he knew that I was thinking about something big. It was in a direction that I'd never considered. The simplicity of it was stunning.

She went on. "You've got to get past the standards of a white collar life. That's over now. You walked away from that when you left the firm in Chicago. You'll have to become a handy-man. This place needs a lot of work. Do you think you're too good to own a little apartment building? Just because the Michigan Business School and the Notre Dame Law School didn't teach construction trades isn't a reason not to learn them."

I looked up at her sparkling eyes, alive and interested, and thought about all of our conversations on the bridge when I was a little boy.

She reached over and patted my knee as she might have when I was little. "We're both changed people. You're not afraid to change some more, are you?"

I leaned back, thinking. Finally I said, "Well, I've learned to prepare the best damn duck in Northern Michigan. Why not be a carpenter, too?"

I knew she was right. I wouldn't make enough money to seriously help my goal of buying the hotel, but it would be a step forward. It would be something that I had done on my own to show Dad. I had saved up twenty-five thousand dollars from cooking and running my thirteen rooms at the hotel last winter.

"I'll see that widow first thing in the morning," I promised Annie.

The widow's small two-story home sat just down the block from Annie, its paint blistered and a "For Sale by Owner" sign stuck in the lawn. I went up to the front door and knocked. A thin, elderly lady with snow-colored hair and a sweet smile opened the door.

"Annie said that you were coming."

As I stood on the broken front step wondering if it was going to cave in, she blurted out, "I've been trying to sell so I can move into a care facility. I haven't had much luck, so I sure hope you buy my houses. I got this house and the apartment building where Annie lives. I'll take eighty-five thousand for both. You want them?"

Stunned, I hesitated, hardly able to believe my good fortune. Her price was way under what I thought they were worth. "Well . . ."

"Alright, I'll do eighty-four thousand, not a penny less, and you don't need much down. I don't need the cash, just the income."

I hadn't planned on buying the second house, but I had stumbled into a great deal. I quickly calculated that my rental income would be up to twenty-five thousand a year less expenses, but I'd keep them low. I'd gotten to be pretty good at being cheap from running my thirteen motel rooms during the previous winter.

"Would fifteen thousand down be enough?"

"That'll do just fine."

I suppressed a big smile as I put out my hand. "It's a deal."

She reached out and shook my hand. "Come on in. I got hot coffee on the stove."

Over coffee, she immediately got down to business. "I heard that you were a lawyer, so you can draw up the contract. My husband got these houses all paid off before he died, so I can sell them on a contract. I trust you. My husband worked for your Dad at the hotel when he first bought it; always said your dad was an honest fellow."

I wished that Joe, who had said that the locals didn't like us, had been there to hear that.

Four cups of coffee later we had ironed out all the details, but my stomach felt like a hole was burning in it. I vowed that no matter how many adorable grandmothers asked me, I was never going to drink coffee again

The houses needed a lot of work and I was anxious to get going. Within a month I was wearing my carpenter's apron, running my saw, and using my square like a regular workman. John was coming by almost daily giving advice and what physical help his failing body could muster. The effects of his heavy drinking were now starting to take their toll, but I was still glad to have his help. Hell, I wouldn't have even known that beams called headers have to go above window and door openings without him.

Toward Christmas, Annie's next door neighbor, another elderly widow, decided to sell me her house for thirty thousand dollars with ten thousand down. That deal depleted my cash, but I was now accumulating a real estate empire.

Along with it, I acquired a pretty shaggy appearance from being too busy to get a haircut or shave. Annie liked my new look, said it made me look free. Free of what, I wasn't sure, but it felt good to wear old clothes and ride around in my beat-up car with Teddy and a back seat full of tools. It didn't matter when I got to work and it didn't matter when I finished. I was the only one doing the work. And Annie and I were remaining good dinner friends, alternating between going out and eating in her pink room.

A few months later, on a January day so cold that my breath almost stuck to my face, I was shoveling snow in front of Annie's gallery, when a neighbor lady hobbled by swinging her cane. "You want to buy my house?" she asked, with a wheeze, a cigarette in her mouth.

I set my shovel down and looked at her marveling at my newly acquired reputation as an old-house-buyer. Before I could say anything she went on, "I'll sell at a good price; don't want any damn real estate people bugging me. How about an even twenty thousand? It's that yellow one across the street," she said, pointing to it over a snow bank.

She had a kind face and I hated to disappoint her. "I'm sorry," I said. "I just don't have any money left."

"Don't matter. I'll sell it to you for nothing down. It has three bedrooms and two baths, in real nice condition. I just baked some cookies and I got hot coffee. Let's sign up a paper, make it legal."

She began to hobble back toward her house before I had even said that I was interested.

"Okay," I yelled. "But I hate coffee."

It was amazing the credit worthiness that I had achieved in Harbor Springs within only a few months. I would now own two houses and a building with an art gallery and three apartments.

CHAPTER 11

WHY NOT A LAUNDROMAT?

Several months later on the last afternoon in March 1981, as I returned home from a day of powdery skiing, the sun hung bright red over the frozen waves of Lake Michigan, casting a pink glow on the snow-covered ground. It calmed and reassured me. Somehow the color pink was beginning to have that effect on me. Perhaps it was Annie's pink apartment, where I always felt content.

Entering my apartment at the hotel, I went straight to the freezer and took out a bottle of gin. I was going to savor those last few minutes of the sunset. I began to pour a nice cold martini when the phone rang. It was Walt.

"Where've you been?" he asked. "I've been trying to reach you since lunch."

I gripped my martini and waited, thinking the zoning deal must have been cut and the bulldozers would be arriving soon. He and Joe had been so cavalier, I was sure they had something up their sleeves, some alternative plan. I knew that they didn't want the contract to expire. But I was so wrong.

"Good news?"

"The deal is off. We're not going to continue this fight."

How could the fellow who wasn't going to take his toys and go home be saying this?

"I'm sorry, but I've spent way too much time and money on this deal already. The locals aren't going to budge on this one. It's not going to happen."

I gulped down my martin, looking out on the bay. But I saw that I wasn't completely surprised. It was just that I'd conned myself into thinking the deal would go through.

"Alright, alright." I gave in, then sighed, not knowing what else to say. "I'll call you back in a few days."

"Okay, but it won't make any difference."

So this was it. My plans had been ruined. And I wondered how I would tell Dad.

I found Annie in her gallery before her big wooden easel set up near the fire as she finished the last strokes on a large oil landscape.

"I thought you didn't like large open landscapes," I said.

"I don't, but sometimes they pay the bills."

I nodded, then went on as if her words hadn't registered, for I couldn't wait another minute without unloading my troubles into her care. "My condominium deal fell through..."

I sat down, my stomach in knots. I had already consumed three martins. Annie fixed me a cup of mint tea to settle my stomach.

"I don't know what to do, and I don't know how to tell Dad."

She sat across from me, pursing her lips. "Why don't you push through the zoning on your own? Your request is reasonable. You'll eventually get the zoning changed."

"But I don't have the money to develop the condominiums myself."

"I didn't say that you had to develop them. Once you've got the rezoning, you could sell the project to Walt or anybody else."

I sat gazing at her. Annie was right. This was a way out. I vowed I wasn't going to be beaten down.

We called out for a pizza and I spent the next couple of hours lounging in front of the fire discussing my options. We agreed that the real problem was the summer association. The owners of the pillared cottages didn't want change. They'd put pressure on the city to keep things the same. What they needed, I realized, was a dose of reality.

"That's it," I exclaimed. "I've got to show them what could be built under the existing zoning. I've got to convince them that we really would do it, build a gas station and convenience store."

But then my excitement faded. The architecture, engineering and surveying documents needed for rezoning, I realized, would be expensive.

"I'd probably have to sell a couple of my rental houses and, if I failed, my money would be wiped out."

"Then why don't you use Walt's zoning documents? Maybe you could talk him into letting you use them in exchange for a right of first refusal once you succeeded."

"That's brilliant! It'll keep things going forward. Even if I fail, it'll buy another year."

I leaned over and kissed her, but she pushed away and gazed at what was left of the embers.

I took my cue. Standing and heading for the door, I said, "Thanks for being my friend, Annie. I don't know what I would do without you."

With that I slipped out into the icy night, torn by excitement and rejection.

The next morning I called Walt and told him that I wanted to continue the zoning battle. I asked if I could use his documents in exchange for Dad extending his purchase option for two years. I reminded him that he'd already sunk a lot of money into the project so he might as well give me a chance.

Walt went on with some questions which I thought to be pointless. His tone was studied indifferent, but I felt that he was buying time to calculate the repercussions of my offer. Good. He was like that, cold and concentrated.

"What makes you think you can succeed?" came the confident voice across the phone.

Even though I now felt a bit rattled, like Walt and I were in the same room and he was standing next to me while I was seated, I answered as if I was thinking aloud, "I'm young, money hungry, and tough. I'll get it through because I don't care what the neighbors say. The present zoning is a screw job. I'll convince everybody that we might really build a gas station or, for that matter, a laundromat."

A chuckle came across the line, followed by a silence which I didn't disturb. Maybe I had finally won his respect. I was sure that my proposal was seriously being considered.

After what seemed to me to be a few minutes, but was probably only thirty seconds, I added, "I'll get Dad so ticked that he might really do it. Then when the association gets sick of the traffic in front of their homes, they'd support a zoning change."

"Well, I don't know."

"You have nothing to lose. I'll name myself as the developer and take all the heat. If I succeed you've got your deal."

"Let me talk to Joe."

"No, this is between you and me; he's got nothing to do with it. I don't want him involved. He's a good ole boy who likes to drink coffee with the locals at the newsstand. No one would believe my threats if he was involved."

"I see."

"Remember, I'm not a resorter or a local. I've never felt like I belonged to either. I'm Dad's kid, and he's got a reputation for being tough and hot-tempered."

"Your bluff might work," said Walt in a chuckle.

"Of course it will, because it's not a bluff."

"Alright, you got a deal."

"Oh, one other thing, Walt." I took a breath. "I want a clause in our new agreement saying that you have only fifteen days to act on your purchase agreement from the time I succeed."

"What happens then?"

"Oh, not much, except all your work, including the site plan, engineering, and legal preparation all become exclusively my property. I just want this protection if I'm going to let them beat me up. You're going to go through with the deal, aren't you?"

"Okay, like you say, what have I got to lose? My secretary will get a new contract out to you in the morning."

On a cold night, one year later, in March 1982, the site plan was finally approved. To win, I'd had to hire one of those high-priced zoning attorneys from a big law firm in Detroit who cost about as much as I'd paid for a down payment on one of my rental buildings some years earlier. But it was worth it. He'd succeeded, and I relished the way that he'd driven home the idea that we'd really build a gas station if we were denied.

After the meeting my attorney set down his horn-rimmed spectacles and went around the room shaking hands with all the zoning board members. He'd won, but he might appear before them again so he still wanted to be liked. But for me it was different. The victory was anti-climactic. During the preceding few months I'd suffered sleepless nights and numerous upset stomachs, as I pursued a single-minded course toward the site plan approval that I knew I'd eventually get. I didn't see any point in pleasantries; they hadn't done anything for me that I wasn't entitled to. The echo of the memory of Dad almost collapsing by those October cattails after the first zoning meeting rang in my mind as I slammed my briefcase shut and walked out of the room.

Returning home, confident that the condos would now be built, I prepared a double martin, lit a blazing fire, and sat down to call Walt. It was now eleven o'clock, but I didn't care. This was big; he could wake up! All the time, money, and headaches were over, I thought. Maybe they could start construction next week, get the units up this summer. Why not? I had done my end of the deal.

Walt was pretty groggy when he answered the phone. "Couldn't this wait till tomorrow?"

"No. Damn it. We won, or rather I won. How soon can you guys start?" I bellowed, not caring about his beauty rest. If he wasn't completely awake, he was now going to be. "Alright," said Walt. "But let me explain some things to you. You don't just get approval and build the next day."

He paused for a second, probably to think of some other excuses. I knew he was going to give me a lecture about patience, something I was in no mood to hear so I cut him off. "Why not?"

"Well, we have to get our sales plan and finances all together."

"Bullshit. We've been at this for almost two years. Good God, I assumed big-time guys like you had everything in order."

"Well, the problem is that things have changed. The economic climate is different than last year."

I sat there staring at the phone. "What the hell do you mean?"

"Calm down. We'll see what we can do. Joe will be in touch with you in a few days."

And with that, the phone went dead.

Joe again. But it was Walt's money, and I would only be selling the units, not building them. It wasn't my call, but I still didn't like it much.

A week later I met Joe in his office above his wife's gift shop, feeling like I had been called to the principal's office. It was small and looked like it had been a storeroom until someone added a window. Joe told me to sit in the chair across from his desk, and he began rubbing his brow.

"Walt and I have been talking. The economy isn't good. We're in a bit of a recession. It would be better to put things off a year."

"What?" I said, standing so abruptly that I bumped the table behind me, jarring a few of his knickknacks there. I let my eyes bore into him while several years of frustration flowed out. "The contract says you have fifteen days to decide. Your option is up in a few days and so are your chances to develop the condos. The site plan, architecture, and all the engineering will be mine. There won't be any next year."

Joe stiffened, straightening his shoulders. "Yeah, maybe so, but what can a kid like you with no money or experience do with all that? In this economy, there won't be any other developers."

"Maybe so, but I've had enough." I wanted to add that it would be nice to get both him and Walt out of my life.

Joe rubbed a hand across his bald head. Maybe I had gotten to him or maybe he was just waiting for the full impact of what had happened to settle in on me. At moment I didn't care. I exhaled a big breath and thought if the deal was ruined, it was worth it. I couldn't stand him.

I stormed out, hearing him say, "Just wait. You'll see, kid. You can't pull this off without us."

That night, sitting on the gallery floor by the fire, I told Annie that I worried that Walt might have been the only developer willing to give Dad a million dollars and that I had let my temper kill the deal. The thought that maybe I should have been willing to wait another year was gnawing at me.

I'd been so obsessed with the rezoning that I'd never considered the possibility Walt might back out. To me, it had been a done deal. Once I got the rezoning I honestly expected the bulldozers to arrive the next week and begin construction. Naïve, perhaps, but I wanted action. That was my nature.

I had already had three martins and needed a fourth. At the time it seemed that everything I had worked for over the last couple of years had slipped away. All of my dreams of owning the hotel had vanished. Oh, the futility of it all. I hadn't cried since I was twelve, when my grandmother died, but now I couldn't hold it back. Tears poured down my cheeks. The condo project was gone and, worse, with it any chance of winning Dad's respect.

"I don't know how to tell Dad that I was the one who killed the deal. I've got to have another drink."

Annie moved closer. "No you don't."

We sat next to each other staring into the fire. Finally, she said, "You'd better go. Come see me in the morning. I've got an idea."

My gin-numbed brain wasn't even curious enough to ask what her idea was and took little comfort in it. Defeated, I rose obediently and made my way home in the cold night.

Chapter 12

The painting

The next morning I arrived back at Annie's gallery with what seemed like two freight trains colliding in my head. Annie was sitting on a canvas drop cloth next to the ashes of last night's fire. I walked over to the fireplace, added a couple more logs, and sat across from her.

"How do you feel?" she said.

"Not good."

She got up and moved to an easel holding a large painting turned toward the wall. "Do you remember the bluff landscape I was working on last year?

"Yeah, it was the view of the bay through some trees. There was a big birch in the middle of it."

"This is it," she said, turning the easel so I could see the painting.

Even in my hung-over condition I was moved by the beauty of the scene. It looked more spectacular than the view from Walt's front porch. "Is it a real place or just some utopian vision?" I asked.

"Yes, it's real. Get your coat on. We're going there. I've wanted to show it to you for some time. And now the time is ripe. Your future might depend on it."

Half an hour later we were a mile from the hotel on the boardwalk passing our bridge, where she'd painted my first St. Bernard and me. We stopped and noticed the mint and watercress alive and flourishing in the icy water, their fresh green making a startling contrast to the dying March snow. For a moment I forgot about gutless Walt killing my deal. Spring was near, and studying the greenery growing against the stream's current, I felt that something new and exciting was coming.

I wondered what Annie had in mind for me. What could a painting from a bluff have to do with my future? But I was sure Annie would find some connection. I had to believe in her. She had told me to buy my houses, and she had told me to handle the rezoning by myself. She had yet to steer me wrong.

For another twenty minutes we climbed the boardwalk, then made our way along the top of the bluff through thick brush where brambles scratched us. After awhile we reached the spot of her painting, which I recognized immediately. It seemed as if we stood in the middle of an impressionistic painting. The morning light slanted through the barren trees, revealing to the south something extraordinary; the single birch, towering above the tops of pine trees that stretched out to meet the still frozen waters of Lake Michigan.

We stood there like mariners contemplating a voyage on a distant sea.

"Look. Even in the winter it's something," said Annie.

She wrapped her scarf around her face to keep out the March wind sweeping up the bluff. "A woman commissioned me to paint this view. I think she was going to hang it over the fireplace in the home that she and her husband were going to build here. But his business failed, they got a divorce, and the house never got built. And I never got paid, which is why I still have the painting."

"What does that have to do with me?"

Annie went on, "Don't you see? This would be a perfect little real estate development. It's just the right size for four homes. I know you can do it. Look at how you fixed up your homes in town."

I stood there listening to the pine trees shaking their needles in the spring wind. "Ket-cha-na-bay," that was John's word for an inspiring view. I was never sure if it was a real Indian word or something that he just made up. Regardless, it fit this place.

Annie turned away from the rising wind and looked me in the eyes. "It's been on the market for one hundred thousand. That's probably scared people off, but you could get it for less. The wife has told me they'll take sixty thousand."

I stood there in the snow thinking. "Winter is a good time to buy. I guess I could just sit on it till I'm ready to develop it."

Annie grabbed my arm. "And you could sell your homes to get the money to develop this. You might be surprised at what you could get for them."

I nodded, but knew that I wasn't ready to sell the only secure things in my life. I grasped Annie's hand and we started to tramp our way out of the woods. When we reached our bridge, she stopped and said, "I've always known that this bridge would lead to something special."

That afternoon I offered sixty thousand dollars for the Bluff and three days later I got it for sixty-eight thousand, with twenty thousand down. The bluff was mine, but any plans for it would have to be put on hold. Spring was here and another summer of cooking lay ahead. But I knew that someday I'd develop it.

Chapter 13

A harvest moon

Five months later on July 22, around eleven o'clock at night, Annie and I were sitting in her pink efficiency celebrating my thirty-first birthday. For me, the summer had meant long, hot hours in the hotel kitchen perfecting duck, and I was looking forward to it ending. But that night I was going to put cooking out of my mind and enjoy the cake Annie had bought me. The white cake with layers of thick white frosting decorated with pink and blue flowers with green stems was sitting on the coffee table in front of us. It was exactly the kind of cake that only a professional baker could make. There was nothing homemade about it and it brought back the memories of my childhood when we had a baker at the hotel who would make this kind of cake for my birthday.

Annie smiled at me, probably remembering when she was my summer girl and that the birthday cake we'd eaten then was so similar to the one she'd purchased. "Remember that first summer I took care of you? Your parents had forgotten your birthday."

"Yeah," I answered with a sigh. "It was no big deal. I just went to the hotel baker and ordered a cake."

"You also picked out a table in the dining room and ordered filet mignons for all the hotel guests' children whom you invited to your party."

"It was better that way. I invited a lot more kids than my parents would have. The presents were great. I liked being in control." I winked.

Annie stared at me. "I remember your mother calling me from the bar. She felt bad."

"Maybe, but I know she was damn proud that I pulled it off by myself. A lot of kids would have whined about missing their birthday, but not me. I just went on with things—like I do today."

I reached across the table and squeezed Annie's hand, realizing that in her I had a friend who truly understood me. Then I looked up into her face, but her expression was guideless. Still, I wondered, what would I ever do without her?

Six weeks later, on the Saturday before Labor Day, Annie and I were sitting in the crowded hotel lounge listening to the piano player's last performance of the season. During breaks in the music I could hear hotel guests and cottage owners seated nearby discussing their plans to leave.

Earlier, while walking the hotel grounds, I had noticed a big moon casting a yellow glow over the bay. Dad always said that kind of moon meant as much to a hotel man as it did to a farmer. "The farmer has his crops in the barn after the harvest, and the hotel man has his money in the bank after the season."

The warmth of the crowd, cigarette smoke, and the general smell of liquor filled the room, but the first briskness of fall seeped through an open window near us in our back corner, causing Annie to shiver. For an instant, she snuggled into me but pulled away, remaining close but not touching. Over the last two years Annie had been my best friend, but I had always wondered why there hadn't been more. Something held her back, but what? I wondered if it was her failed marriage, our age difference, or her aversion to settling down. Looking back, I think it was combination of the three. But at the time I couldn't understand. I wanted Annie and might have married her if she'd had me.

For Annie, it had been another summer of becoming reacquainted with Mrs. Baldwin. I would watch the two of them having dinner, thinking that if ever two people were soul mates on earth, it was them.

Mrs. Baldwin had been close with Jennifer, but that had been more as a guide and mentor. Annie and Mrs. Baldwin had both lived life fully and were on a more common footing. Mrs. Baldwin had spent most of her life alone, and it appeared that Annie was choosing to do the same. Mrs. Baldwin had eventually married her lost love. I wondered if there was someone out there for Annie. If so, I suspected it wasn't me.

The evening was wearing on and, as he always did before closing, our long-time entertainer was about to shift to the old sentimental favorites. "Pardon me, I got to pay some bills," crooned Randy Carmichael. This was an inside joke for the resorters and anyone else who knew that he was Hoagie Carmichael's son and that he was about to perform his father's most famous song, Stardust, a song that, because of his father's shrewdness, still generated royalties for Randy. While Randy was pausing for effect and watching to see the smiles glimmering on the faces of those who got it, Annie leaned toward me. Her eyebrows bent a bit as she squinted in the amber light of the cocktail lounge. "Your Dad is now seventy. I've watched him this summer. He's so different than when I worked here twenty-three years ago."

Randy began to sing, "Sometimes I wonder why I spend the lonely nights ..." but Annie kept talking. "He's like a ticking bomb ready to go off. He won't wait much longer. You've got to sell your houses and start developing your bluff property before it's too late."

Annie had guided me right thus far. But those houses were my anchor, I felt, and dug in my heels.

"I don't want to sell my houses. They're my only real security. I'm making good money off them."

She leaned toward me, whispering. "You've got to move now. Your condo deal has been dead since March. I don't see your Dad hanging on much longer if you don't show him a plan."

I stared down at the table, not wanting to face what she was saying. Life was pretty good at the moment. I had a couple of good second cooks and was enjoying being the chef. My rental income after expenses was almost thirty-five thousand a year, and Dad was paying me twenty-five thousand for a summer. That was three times what I was making back at the law firm.

I had plenty of time for skiing, had a met a few girls, and had Annie as my best friend, though I still hoped that Annie and I might someday become more than friends. Things were going along okay, and I didn't want to upset that.

But I sensed that Annie was right, that time was running out. I would have to take a gamble and sell my rentals. I had to move forward. Then suddenly it hit me; I could make enough money from the four houses at the bluff over the next two years to develop the hotel condos on my own. The little commissions that Walt would have paid me paled in comparison to the profits from the whole deal. I'd make enough to buy the hotel for cash.

Resting my hand on her leg, I leaned toward Annie. "I can see it. As always, you're right. I can do it. Thank you."

I kissed her tenderly. She pulled back, but kept staring at me as if thinking.

Seconds passed that seemed like hours. Finally she said, "You know that Mrs. Baldwin and I have become close. Even when I was your summer girl she thought that I should become an artist. Art is my life and I need to pursue it, just like the hotel is your life. You need to move forward with the bluff and I need to move forward with my art. I've painted enough clapboard cottages, sailboats, and views of the bay. It's time for me to go."

I felt my face becoming still as I stared back at her. I was stunned, hardly believing what I was hearing. She'd been my friend and confidant these last two years. How would I go on without her? I felt an emptiness much worse than when Jennifer left. I saw that Jennifer had just been a fling, someone to fill a temporary void in my life. But Annie had been a true friend, someone who had guided me in making hard decisions, someone who had helped me make solid plans for the future.

I had known when I first met her back in the gallery that her time in Harbor Springs was finite. She always made that clear. But I hadn't thought about her really going. It just seemed like a vague, abstract thing in the future, kind of like death. I knew it was there, but didn't think about it.

Annie leaned closer, kissed me on my cheek, and took a breath.

"Mrs. Baldwin has sponsored me for an internship with the National Art Institute in Washington, D.C., and I've been accepted. I have to be there in two weeks."

I looked at her, thinking how she had looked after me as a child, seeing that I didn't get hurt and that I made the right decisions. Now she had been doing the same for me as an adult. I wondered how many people get to have that.

Annie broke the silence. "I want you to have my paintings of the bridge and the bluff. That part of my life is over, but for you it's just beginning."

"Thanks, but I can't believe you're leaving. I thought—I hoped we might stay together."

Grasping my hand, she said, "We probably won't spend much more time together. I've got a lot to do. But I want to tell you something."

My God, I thought, she's giving advice right up to the end.

"A lot of folks don't know what they want out of life, including me. That's why I have wandered around, until perhaps now. But you're lucky. You know exactly what you want—this hotel. I don't want you to lose it. And—you've got to find someone who fits your life. Jennifer was too young, with big plans ahead of her. I'm too old. I've already done all that stuff. You need to find somebody who has ties to this area and loves this hotel."

After a final hug we got up and left the lounge. Annie walked home alone and I headed up the back stairs to my room, and a winter of just me and Teddy Bear.

The next morning I placed ads in the local paper for all my houses. The house with Annie's gallery sold in the first week to an antique dealer who loved the pink color. By the time Annie left, I had contracts on the other three houses as well. I hated to part with them, but the two hundred and fifty thousand dollars that I cleared after paying off the mortgages would give me enough money to build my first two houses at the bluff.

One morning a few weeks after Annie left, I entered Dad's box-car sized office, its paneled walls covered with pictures of the hotel, its guests, old employees, and grand buffets. It was hard to find one that didn't have either Dario or Benny in it.

With the hotel closed, there was no one else around. Dad sat at his big desk scrutinizing a document that had come from one of the files piled high in front of him. After a bit of conversation about the season, I walked up to the front of his desk. Dad didn't keep an extra chair in his office because he didn't want anybody sitting down and visiting, so standing before him, I blurted out, "I've sold all of my rental property and got a pile of cash. I'm going to start building two houses on my bluff in a few weeks. If I pull this off, I'll have enough money to build the condos at the hotel and, remember, I already have an approved site plan."

It felt awkward trying to get the right words out. But I knew that I had to present a plan or Dad might sell. I had to let him know that I was serious about moving forward, so I walked around to the side of his desk and stood next to him. "They say there's a recession, but look what I've done. Give me a chance. I know I can do it."

Dad lowered his reading glasses and looked up from the document he'd been reading. His facial expression was uncommitted so I couldn't tell whether I had gotten to him. Then unexpectedly he smiled at me. "You're still going to be the chef, aren't ya? I can't run the hotel without you in the kitchen."

I knew that was Dad's way of telling me that I had more time. He wasn't the kind of guy who was just going to say yes. I think his ego always required things to be somewhat ambiguous in his favor so that he could keep control till the last minute. But I had made my point, and Dad admitted that he needed me.

"Yeah, I'll keep cooking. I've sort of grown accustomed to it."

"You going to grow your hair and not shave again this winter?"

"Nah, I don't think so. That was when I was a handyman. Now I'm a developer."

Dad adjusted his glasses and picked up the paper that he'd been reading. I stepped back and looked at him. His hair had turned much whiter, and the blue in his eyes had dulled to gray. He was no longer the guy who could have beaten up the world. Annie was right; there wasn't a lot of time. He was a man looking to quit.

As I walked out into the lobby, Dad yelled after me, "And the food better be good next summer."

I smiled and thought, damn, I got another year.

CHAPTER 14

THE ELMER FUDD HAT

A few weeks later I hired a builder to construct my first two homes at the bluff. He was a talented young fellow and offered to let me work with his crew during the construction. Since my deal was based on T and M, time and materials, I was able to save the wages of a laborer because that was all I was good for at first. But more important I was able to create a productive hurry-up work atmosphere, which saved thousands of desperately needed dollars.

As winter approached I purchased some brown insulated overalls and a red and white Elmer Fudd hat with flaps on all four sides. I spent the days at the project pounding nails and hauling materials, just the same as the rest of the crew.

During the dead of the winter of 1983 Teddy and I would get to the bluff extra early in the dark morning and fire up the builder's old pot-bellied stove with scrap wood so I could have hot coffee ready for the men when they arrived by eight. I'd sit and chug down a couple of cups with them every morning. (Once again, despicable coffee served as a social lubricant. In small-town Michigan, it just couldn't be avoided.) It was great bonding, and I think they liked me. I wasn't like a usual rich developer, and they appreciated it. They sure worked their butts off for me. They were all good guys and taught me a hell of a lot about carpentry. On those icy days when my hammer would slip and hit my finger, I'd stifle a yelp and comfort myself by thinking how much I had learned about the building trades.

I figured that someday it would be of value in negotiating large contracts when I actually built the condominiums at the hotel.

But now I realize that I gained far more. For a person who had been totally left-brained, I acquired a sense of creativity, something that I would carry forward the rest of my life. I learned to transfer an idea from paper to reality. I could tell what would look good and what wouldn't.

With being able to ski only on the weekends, it seemed that the winter would drag on forever. But I didn't feel lonely because I was too busy during the days and too tired at night to socialize. After early dinners at McDonald's or the local Chinese restaurant, I'd spend an hour sitting in a hot bath trying to take the stabbing aches out of my over-educated and under-conditioned body. Then it'd be time for bed so I could do the same thing the next day.

Eventually winter did end, and by early July the first of my two gray wood-and-stone homes was complete, and the other was finished on the outside. But I was running out of money because the infrastructure of ground prep, roads, electricity, telephone, TV, sewer and water had cost a lot more than I had budgeted. So I decided to leave the second house as a shell, at least giving the impression that it was done. With the sod, shrubs, and geraniums in place, no one would be the wiser, especially since I had nailed sheets inside the windows so no one could see the unfinished walls. I thought that two homes finished and stakes marking the spots for the next two homes lent an impression of success. I had started a genuine real estate development, not just a spec-house.

In all of the hours huddled up with Annie by the winter fire in the gallery, making plans for my Hansel and Gretel homes, we hadn't once discussed what it would really be like to sell them. I assumed that once my unique homes with their heart-stopping view were finished, a few ads in the local paper would sell them as quickly as they had my earlier remodeled houses. But that wasn't the case.

My next line of attack was to put highway signs directing people into my project. This was a common tactic used by most developers, so I thought it would work.

Since I had promised Dad that I'd still be the chef, I had only my afternoons free. I spent every hour hanging out at the bluff, sitting in the one house that was complete and hoping that my signs would snatch someone off the road who might really buy. But that wasn't to be. Tourists came in to see how rich resorters lived or to simply look out at the red, white, and blue spinnakers pulling yachts over the dark blue waters of Little Traverse Bay.

I grew tired of explaining that spinnakers weren't just for style, that they captured the light air of our bay and sped up a boat on down-wind. Parents would nod and point, asking which boat was in the lead, while their children thought it was fun to kick my newly painted walls. Clearly these folks weren't going to buy. This wasn't working any better than the ads in the paper, and I knew it. There had to be a better way.

I reasoned that, since the Colonial Inn had never been marketed to the general public, why should the bluff? The hotel had an air of exclusivity about it, so why shouldn't my homes? They were adorable right down to the curved window and bird houses built into their gabled roofs.

I thought about how Dad never missed an opportunity to drum up business and puzzled on how I might do the same.

I remembered that Dad wasn't shy about promoting his business, even on the golf course. He made sure his foursomes were always short one or two, and he prowled the pro shop and starter's office for others to join them. Usually these people would be staying at other hotels, and Dad would then treat them as if they had been long-time friends and lure them to the Colonial Inn.

It was then I remembered Annie's painting hanging in my apartment, and an idea came to me. I brought the painting down, placed it on an easel at the entrance to the dining room, and affixed a sign saying "Dream for Sale." Then at night I began cruising the dining room in my chef's attire promoting my homes.

Within a week, I sold my first house to a couple from Nashville staying at the hotel while checking out a yacht. Hearing that they had made inquiries about the bluff, I personally came out from the kitchen to carve their chateaubriand. The next morning I drove them up to my bluff where they fell in love with the view and decided to buy.

A few days later I sold my second home to a couple attending a dinner party at the hotel. The hostess had enjoyed my lamb shanks so much that she called me out of the kitchen to meet her guests. I came carrying with me my bluff brochures. The hostess laughed and pointed to a couple sitting at the other end of the table, saying that they had been looking for a summer home in Harbor Springs. Everyone had a good laugh at the chef who sold real estate, but the couple met me the next morning and we soon closed the deal.

Thanks to Annie's painting and a lot of chutzpa, I would now have the money to finish the next two homes.

On the hotel's last night of the season, Sunday of Labor Day weekend, 1983, I was making my final rounds through the dining room saying goodbye to all the guests. Dad, wearing his red sports coat, came over to me in the middle of the dining room, slapped me on the back, and boasted, "Tim's going to finish his bluff homes next summer, and by '85 he'll build the condominiums at the Colonial Inn."

I beamed, then fought back tears. I knew this was as close as Dad would get to giving his approval or saying that he was proud of me. Instead of pulling me aside and giving his permission, Dad had announced to the entire dining room that he would actually allow me to build the condominiums at the hotel, the first time I'd heard of it. And this time I didn't have to go to his office and stand hat-in-hand before his oversized desk. But I still had no guarantee that he'd ever sell me the hotel.

CHAPTER 15

A HORN ON A WHEELCHAIR

I think 1984 was a good year. I don't remember it well, only a blur of work and sleep, but I have good feelings about it. There were no zoning battles, major conflicts with Dad, nor entanglements with women, just a steady progression forward toward my ultimate goal of owning the hotel. During the summer I sold my last two homes at the bluff and in the fall I began what I thought was my final step. The bulldozers and back-hoes rolled in scourging the green hotel grounds for the footings of the condominiums.

In June 1985 with the condominiums nearing completion, I thought that all I had to do to sell them was begin contacting folks from my extensive list of prospective buyers. Unlike the local indifference to my bluff homes, talk of the Colonial Inn condominiums, although not always positive, had been on the front burner of Harbor Springs' society for almost five years. Publicity from the highly contentious zoning battles had lit a fire that hadn't dimmed. The more commentary, the more people wanted to buy--or so I thought.

Continually, I heard it said that if the town and the summer association wanted to block my development, then it must be special. Not wanting to be left out, over two hundred people had said they definitely wanted to buy as soon as I had units available. At the time it seemed that I'd be flooded with sales. But I was dreadfully naive.

The people who had been impressed by all the publicity turned out to be rubber-neckers, with no real money. Not one of them wanted to commit. Looking back, I can see that it had all been conversation to look good and play the big shot. These people wanted to feel that they too had the money to buy in a place where others had been summering for generations. Why not say they'd take one of the units? It sounded impressive and cost nothing. But in the end it made me mad.

But now I can see that the problem was largely my fault. I hadn't yet gained the ability to discern who had the money and a reason to buy. The people who later bought the units would never have announced their intention to do so in the hotel dining room.

As I crossed names off my list with each successive phone call, I became more discouraged. After a hundred rejections I began to wish that I hadn't built the condominiums and instead had offered Dad the money from my bluff homes as a down payment on the hotel. At the time I thought Dad might have actually sold on an installment contract if I'd only asked. I desperately regretted that I had rolled the dice instead. But the really big money for the condominiums was out there, and I wanted it.

In retrospect I realize that I had done the right thing in going for the big prize, and I would tell any young person to do the same. I see now that Dad would never have sold on an installment contract. He would have considered it way too risky to place his life's work in the hands of a thirty-two-year-old kid. I hadn't had a chance to prove myself yet. I didn't know it, but there were other challenges waiting.

By the Fourth of July I still hadn't sold a unit. I cruised the bar and dining room at night, putting forth the same effort that I had done for the bluff. But this time it didn't work. This project was much larger, and I was young and inexperienced. No one wanted to be the first to take a chance. I hadn't realized it yet, but the negative comments of the neighbors had taken their toll on the kind of people who could actually buy.

One bird-chirping morning, hurrying across the hotel porch to the condos, I saw Mrs. Baldwin, now ninety-five and confined to a wheelchair because of a stroke. I sat on the porch railing next to her to visit. I could always spare a few moments for an old friend, and she had arrived only the day before. Anyway, the rushing around was only for my benefit, to feel a sense of urgency, as if someone was waiting to buy. But looking across the grounds at the condominium model, I could see that, as usual, no one was waiting for me.

Mrs. Baldwin pointed her long thin finger up at the gables over the third floor porches of the condos. "Those bird houses that you tucked up under the roofs—do any birds actually use them?"

"Sometimes, but they're actually just to look cute."

She nodded and pointed to the controls on the arm of her electric wheel chair. "Could you help me get this contraption over to the condominiums? It's been a year, but I'm still not comfortable with it. I'd like to have a look. You have any ground floor units left?"

I wondered what she meant. At her age and health she couldn't have any interest in buying. But what the heck, I'd show her around. At least she would be somebody going through my model and maybe give the impression that I had a live one.

The night before, I had barely held back from slugging a guy in the hotel lounge for calling my project a big white elephant. It was a good thing that I had only had three martins. With four, I might have done it.

I looked down at my old friend. "I haven't sold any."

She smiled up at me. "Then we had better hurry while there're still some left. Now be a dear and help me down the ramp. I can't go flying down it by myself."

As she powered her wheel chair into a ground floor unit and began navigating through its rooms, it seemed to me as though she was experiencing a sense of independence. After some moments of traveling about she looked at me with a big smile and exclaimed, "Finally, a place I can live in. The hotel is not enough now that I have to travel with a maid. I'll take it."

I stared at her. My disbelief must have shown, because she said, "Honey, don't worry about my age. That'll be my heirs' problem. I want this condominium now. How quickly can we get it furnished?"

"A few days. I'll make some calls. But you haven't even asked the price."

"One hundred and forty-nine thousand, I heard you tell someone last night. Now don't try to jack it up on me. Remember, I used to be a broker. Give me a purchase agreement. I'll look it over and sign it this afternoon."

She backed her wheel chair out the door and turned. "Since I'm going to be part of this, I want to get these other units sold. I'm a social person, got to have neighbors. I'm going to get the word out that these units are fine. The neighbors need to quit yakking and come by and take a look. These units would make great guest cottages."

What? Market my development to the very people who had opposed me? But then I saw she was right. These were the people who could afford them and had a reason to buy.

She went on, "My father built some of the first condominiums in Washington D.C. We were ostracized by the church, country club, and anything else that could exclude people. It was terrible! My mother hated it. In time things quieted down, but there was one big thing different. My father now had a lot of money."

I smiled. That sounded good to me.

Ten minutes later I rushed into Dad's office, where as usual, he sat behind his old desk.

"Mrs. Baldwin is going to buy my first unit."

Dad lowered his glasses and squinted at me. "What?"

I could hear his secretary pounding the typewriter in the adjacent office.

"She's my best account and you're taking her away? I can't believe it. Do you have any idea what that's going cost me?"

I stood before him speechless. He went on, brief and to the point, "Well, let me tell you something. Mrs. Baldwin and her maid occupy two rooms for the whole summer. That's over a hundred and forty room nights, equivalent to a convention. And I'm going to lose her now because of you. Thanks; thanks a lot."

I swallowed. After Dad had publicly and proudly announced my condo project to the hotel patrons two years earlier, I had felt he was solidly behind me. Now I felt like he'd stabbed me in the back. I turned and walked away. I didn't want to feel it, but at that moment I hated him and the only thing that kept me going, was knowing one day I'd show him.

A few days later I was driving Mrs. Baldwin back from our closing at the title company. She now owned the condominium and I had a little financial breathing room. It had all gone quite smoothly since it was a cash sale. As we rounded a curve and the bay stretched out in front of us, Mrs. Baldwin announced, "I want to have a dinner party for twelve tomorrow night to show my place off to a few of our neighbors."

As she recited her guest list, my shoulders tensed as I stared out at the whitecaps. "Most of these people have been openly opposed my condos."

Mrs. Baldwin cocked her head. "Yes, but they are still your neighbors, and their friends and relatives are far more likely to buy your units than people who happen to come by because of advertising. You need these folks. Holding grudges won't get your condos sold."

I took it all personally, too personally, I saw, to be a good businessman. "Okay, I get it."

"And after we soften them up with cocktails and rack of lamb, we'll go over to my new condominium for Crepes Suzettes."

I turned toward her and began to laugh. "We'll do it. And I'll light a roaring fire in your big stone fireplace."

Mrs. Baldwin then began explaining the importance of decorum and the perception of propriety. She said that I needed to dine with them, not be the chef. She was going to put her stamp of approval on me, and it wouldn't do for me to smell of lamb. "You've simply got to look the part."

Where had I heard that before? I thought of Dario in his gold checkered chef's coat standing at the end of the buffet and Allen with his crewneck sweater tied around his neck strolling the association grounds.

I tried to remember the last time I actually ate in the dining room— not since Dario had been the chef. She went on, "You'd better read *Time, Newsweek,* and the *Wall Street Journal.* You need to sound like you've been to graduate school. My friends don't want to hear about duck."

"My cooking skills helped sell my first two houses at the bluff."

"That was only two sales," she said. "We have have bigger goals now."

The next evening, wearing my navy blazer, I dined under the brass chandeliers with Mrs. Baldwin and her guests.

"Yes, I used to play golf at Weque and would again soon, when I finished selling all my condominiums," I told them while sipping a martin. I had wanted to add that I had been runner up for the first flight championship at eighteen, but didn't, thinking that that might have been too much. In my moment of glory I had forgotten or simply didn't want to think about the fact that I had only been allowed to play at the club as a teenager under my parents' membership. They had joined long ago when the club wasn't so snobby and even a few locals were let in. Dad had used his membership to play golf with his hotel guests and occasionally even our mailman. If I had thought about it, I would have realized that many in the club probably now wished that Dad and Mother didn't belong and that even making a lot of money would never make me acceptable. After all, it's a matter of birth and social connections that makes you worthy, not the vulgarities of money. This is because some of their members don't really have money so birth and social connections are all important.

The folks in Weque and on the Point have a delightful way of showing this, which many visitors simply don't get, and that's okay. Family status is best shown by driving around in an old car, say a brown 1968 Cadillac Fleetwood or an olive green 1962 Ford Falcon. But the cars have to be in near new condition, like the way they were when your grandfather bought them. Your car can never have been restored because you are trying to say that it's simply been your summer car that's been left in your caretaker's garage every winter.

Your family is so wealthy that you're not concerned about the car. After all, it's just transportation—something to get you around town and to the golf or tennis club. Your family has thought of the car that way since your grandfather drove it up from Oklahoma City or St. Louis back in the 1960's. It may have a few dents and dings—quite acceptable, like the time Uncle Henry backed into the fence post or parked too close to the wrought iron frame of the Colonial Inn canopy. For years everyone who mattered would look at the dents and smile, knowing that they occurred while Uncle Henry was well under the influence of alcohol and probably yelling "Boomer Sooner Schooner" or some other old college fight chant.

To further prove that you didn't just buy someone else's old car, your back window is covered with little round stickers of a bent pine tree, the annual emblem of belonging to the prestigious Little Harbor Club. No one ever takes off a past sticker of having belonged to this dining and tennis club. That would be tantamount to driving a new Mercedes Benz or even wearing a Rolex watch, which simply isn't done on our side of the bay.

That said, the folks on our side of the bay still want you to think that they have a lot of money just like the *nouveau riche* folks on the other side of the bay. They just have a quaint way of doing it. My neighbor in his thirty-year-old wood paneled station wagon may only have use of it, the various club memberships and the cottage for only his annual week. Back home he may be loaded with as much credit card debt as the Mercedes-Rolex owner across the bay, but you're not supposed to figure that out.

Sometimes you have to add new money to the old money, and some of these folks haven't done that in years. Hence, even in 2012, both Harbor Point Golf Club and Wequetonsing Golf Club allow the public to play on their hallowed grounds in the fall and spring when the resorters for the most part are gone. Why not? That bit of extra green fees helps reduce their membership costs, which they apparently need, and they're not here to see those people play anyway.

When the dinner was served, I bit into a lamb chop, hoping that my second cook hadn't over-cooked it, and nodded in agreement while the conversation drifted from golf to what a fine job Ronald Reagan was doing. Still trying not to worry about the kitchen, I was about to interject some comment which I thought might be clever when I noticed Dad standing a few tables away watching.

My hand instinctively went to straighten my tie. I knew that by actually dining with these guests I was violating his protocol and, although he didn't say anything, coming from an old way of doing things, it had to have bothered him. In a way, I understood because, in spite of how close I was becoming with Mrs. Baldwin, I could never have called her by her first name. It just wouldn't have seemed right.

When we got up to move to Mrs. Baldwin's condominium for dessert, I thought about how nice it had been to have something to talk about besides zoning, construction, and cooking.

The next morning one of the dinner guests came by to see the condominiums. With little haggling, he bought one as a guest cottage. When I told Mrs. Baldwin, she smiled in a grandmotherly way.

"We'll get two sales out of the next party."

After holding court at her next party, Mrs. Baldwin was attempting to steer her wheel chair through our crowded lobby to the lounge while holding a heavily whipped-creamed Irish coffee. When someone backed into her, the dark brown coffee ended up covering her from chest to lap, ruining her pink dress. She said good night to her guests and retired as if nothing had happened.

The next morning Mother purchased a bicycle horn for her, which I installed on the arm of her wheel chair. Mrs. Baldwin wanted to try it immediately. As guests gathered around, I was amazed to see that she didn't have the strength to squeeze the red rubber ball. Mrs. Baldwin's commanding presence had blinded me to how frail her body had become. Mother offered to get her an electric horn, but Mrs. Baldwin refused.

"No, just have someone follow me and squeeze the damn thing!"

Thereafter I assigned a busboy to follow her from the dining room to the bar, his hand constantly on the red ball. She had him honk every few feet, announcing her arrival into the cocktail lounge.

During the summer of 1985 I sold eight of the twelve units in my first building, with Mrs. Baldwin assisting in six sales. It was hard to believe that I had done so well. I had enough money to start the second and final building, twelve more units for the next season.

I thought Dad would have been pleased. I was rapidly moving toward the day when I could buy the hotel. But he wasn't. On closing morning in early September as I was shutting down the old black cast-iron stoves after breakfast, Dad entered the kitchen. He stood there across from the steam table and stared at me. "You're killing the goose that laid the golden egg. Three of your sales, including Mrs. Baldwin, were long term guests of mine. I'll be losing their room revenue next summer. Thanks."

I kept on wiping down the stove in front of me, wishing that he would just go away. I had planned a long bike ride to Wilderness Beach that afternoon, kind of a closing ritual. I'd walk the beach, take stock of my life, comparing where I had been and where I was going. Closing day is the time for a hotel man to do those kinds of things. I still do it, even today. Each season is like a chapter in my life. I have to properly end it. But this time Dad had written a different ending for me.

He went on, "You've spent way too much time on Mrs. Baldwin and not enough on the other guests. They pay, too, you know. You remember what happened to Herman Silverstein's flower shops? Well, it looks like it's happening here. If you had only stayed in Chicago..."

Chapter 16

On top of the world

Fall 1985 passed quickly as I began construction on my next twelve units. What with the usual hassles with plumbers, electricians, and drywallers, I hardly even noticed the leaves falling. We poured the footings on a hot day in early September, and the next thing I remember was the first snows of November. When I had been with Annie, I'd seen the deeper gold in the leaves each day. But now I buried myself in my mission of completing my condominiums, filling my days with work and my nights with dreams of getting rich.

By Christmas the roof was complete, and we began trimming and painting, which gave me time to ski. The second building went up much easier than the first because I now knew at least the rudiments of construction. I had no girl, but I didn't care and I wasn't lonely like I had been six years earlier during the winter of 1980. I was too busy to be melancholy.

On February afternoons, late in the day when shadows darkened the ski slopes, I'd be making my last run as the sun hung orange in the big winter sky. I'd stop about a third of the way down, wait for the last of the skiers to pass, look down over Little Traverse Bay, and think. Unbelievable! I was really pulling this goddamn thing off. Six years earlier I had been an associate in a big law firm and miserable. Now I was somebody.

By the next fall, I'd sold ten more units, again thanks to a lot of help from Mrs. Baldwin. I now had only six more in my entire project to sell.

But that was where most of my profits lay, so I still wasn't in a position to buy the hotel. The market for upscale real estate in Harbor Springs at that time was purely summer-driven. What wasn't sold by September would remain so until next summer. But that was okay. I didn't feel that Dad was quite ready to sell anyway. With my confidence growing, I thought, what's wrong with another year? With nothing to do, I figured that I might enjoy a winter in Harbor Springs. I'd have plenty of time for skiing and even girls.

When the January skies of the winter of 1987 cleared and the dry crispness of February arrived, I would again pause on my last ski run of the day and think. I thought about the girls I was seeing and how none of them compared to Annie or Jennifer, who now seemed so far in the past. I thought about how Mrs. Baldwin had helped them and how back in those days I would have never thought how important she would become in my life. And I worried about Mrs. Baldwin. I didn't face it, but she'd looked terribly frail last September. On that parting morning when I had lifted her from her wheelchair to the front seat of her station wagon, she felt only like dead weight.

But I didn't dwell on it. I just offered up a silent prayer of thanks and imagined Mrs. Baldwin living forever. Why not? I was going to. I was now so close to my dream of buying the hotel, I couldn't imagine it not happening. I was almost there.

Just a few months later the woods in Northern Michigan were alive with white trilliums. On a Saturday morning in late May 1987, as I sat in my condominium model, I again felt that I had achieved it all. On that day the future looked limitless and bright. I was on top of the world. I stared out at the hotel pool and the greenness of the surrounding grounds. Looking over at the green-and-white-striped canopy of the hotel, the majestic trees, its lush lawn, I felt sure that all I saw would be mine by the end of season. It was simply a matter of time.

White sprawling clouds lazed about the early morning sky which was filled with a big bright sun. The warmth of the morning made me want to go down to the hotel beach and dig my toes into the warm sand of the new season. But I felt pressed to stay where I was. There were still more sales to make.

Also I was still worried about Mrs. Baldwin. She had called the day before saying she expected to arrive on opening day, in about a month. But her voice had sounded so frail.

The front door to my model opened without a knock and a young girl entered. She looked like she belonged in one of the nearby three-story beachfront "cottages" with a mahogany speedboat tied to the dock. Her red sundress and blonde hair moved as if windblown as she stepped toward me.

"You must be Tim, I'm Wendy."

I decided to remain seated as she didn't look like a buyer. "Nice to meet you."

"I'm staying in my father's cottage. Dick Johnson; you know him?"

"Yeah, I know your Dad," I said, remembering her father's negative comments at that first zoning meeting. A New York investment banker, with his silver hair perfectly combed and smooth manner, he'd seemingly enjoyed every bit of my demise that cold October night. He'd been rather smug about it, too, joking loudly on the way out of the meeting.

Wendy said, "I'll be here for the whole summer. Our cottage is just down from your beach and I need a job. Got any openings?"

Her blue eyes sparkled with excitement. For a moment I totally forgot about being thirty-five with a bit of grey hair. I felt young again like no time had passed since college. She was beautiful, yeah, but she had presence. The rumors that her mother had been an actress must have been true.

"I'm amazed you're here. I didn't think your Dad cared much for me."

"Oh you mean the zoning stuff years ago."

I nodded with a sheepish grin, not wanting to delve into the subject. I was way too happy to bring up old wounds.

"Well, you got your project. That was then, this is now, and you're going to get rich, if you haven't already. Can't you forgive and forget? Have a little heart and give a girl a job. I'm a pretty good waitress."

Three things were evident to me. One, she was gorgeous. Two, the waitress staff had already been hired well in advance of the season, but I was going to hire her anyway. Three, I liked being called rich. Having cooked food and washed dishes, I hadn't thought of myself that way before. This new power was exhilarating.

"Well, I don't know if we can use you. Tell me about yourself. Where do you go to school?"

"I'll be a senior at The University of Michigan, where you went."

"How do you know that?"

"From my father, you know, he actually respects you."

I stared at her. "Really?"

"He respects people who succeed and win. That's you, isn't it?"

I gave her a big grin. "Yes, I did win in the end."

She smiled back at me. "I'm an art history major but will be going to law school in New York next year. I can hardly wait. Wasn't law school so intellectual?"

"How did you know that I was a lawyer?"

"My father. I told you that he'd been impressed with you."

I remembered actually liking law school, with its subtle intrigues; it was just the drudgery of practicing law that I had despised. "Yeah, I loved the mental gymnastics of law school. It was fun reasoning the cases of shipwrecked sailors who had turned cannibal, then later argued duress as a defense."

"How near death do you have to be to eat someone?"

"I'm not sure. We'd have to put on white wigs and go back in time to London to argue it."

She laughed. "That'd be something. But if you give me a job we could talk more about it."

I could see each little pearl on her necklace move as she spoke.

"Okay, you're hired," I blurted, then without thinking, added, "Do you want to go sailing? The wind is perfect."

I sat there feeling aflutter, as she seemed to appraise me. Finally she spoke, "Sure. Dad's away and it's lonely in our big cottage."

A half hour later I'd swum out to my faded red sailboat bobbing on its mooring. I'd had the eighteen foot center board Rebel since I was in junior high school and still loved her. Even with all the success I'd had in real estate, I'd never thought of getting rid of her.

I climbed up onto the boat, unhitched her from the mooring and paddled her toward our dock where Wendy was waiting. My heart pounded as I noticed that she was wearing only a little red bikini under her white tee shirt. Red, tan, and blonde were fast becoming my favorite colors. A few moments later I had the boat against the dock and she climbed in. We pushed off, and I hoisted up the main sail and pulled the jib up into the blue sky.

As the beach shrank into the distance, I grabbed a bottle of Bordeaux from my duffle bag that I kept in the bow. "Would you like some? It's big and chewy."

She nodded. "Yes." Then she looked at me. "This is quite day. I got a job, learned to justify cannibalism, and met a fascinating guy with a sailboat."

"Do you think so?"

"That cannibalism can be justified?"

"No. Do you think I'm interesting?"

"The word was fascinating, and the answer is yes, but don't let it go to your head."

The rest of the afternoon Wendy talked about her life as if she'd known me forever. She described the apartment she wanted in the upper east side of New York, followed by a brown-stone later with two kids and a nanny. She would become a famous environmental lawyer and throw intimate cocktail parties for the social elite.

The afternoon slipped by as we skimmed the blue waters of Little Traverse Bay, surrounded by dark green-pined hills. The sun hung low as it didn't want to surrender to the darkness of evening.

"I don't want this day to end," I said.

"Neither do I," murmured Wendy, the growing wind in her face. "Come for dinner. We'll light a fire. It'll be just wonderful. Can you get some steaks from the hotel? I've got everything else."

"Yes." I nodded.

Looking at her, I remembered that I hadn't had a serious girlfriend since college.

"That'd be perfect."

When we reached the mooring, the wind had died to nothing, but out to the west past the mouth of the bay the storm clouds that I'd been watching now loomed big and purple on the open part of Lake Michigan. To me, they looked like the kind that John would have said the Indians took seriously. Wendy noticed them, too, and suggested that we not waste the time to paddle the boat into dock as I would also have to paddle it back to the mooring. I thought it sweet that she was concerned that I might get caught in the storm. She already appeared to be caring at least a little about me. With her eyes straight at me, she laughed. "I'll race ya."

Once on shore, I stood there dripping, but not feeling cold, my gaze on her thin, wet tee-shirt. Her eyes met mine for an instant. It's okay, they seemed to say. Look if you want.

"I'll see you in a few," she whispered, then ran off toward her cottage.

A half hour later, a bottle of wine in one hand and a tray of chateaubriand in the other, I was walking up the long steps to Wendy's cottage. I scarcely even noticed them as I took them two at a time while looking up at her waiting on the porch, which was big enough to hold a cocktail party of at least twenty-five.

Inside the living room, the only light came from a small fire in a massive stone fireplace which Wendy must have just lit. But it produced enough light for me to see that the room wasn't finished in the sense of a modern home. The back of the exterior siding was exposed, with the stud framing totally visible, as was the custom with summer cottages of the late 1800's. While creating a wonderful unfinished look, it wouldn't have passed the first phase of a building inspection, yet it had served their family for a hundred years.

When she finished showing me through the three-story white clapboard cottage, which seemed to ramble endlessly with its fourteen bedrooms and now unused servants quarters, she paused. "Don't you just love old things?"

I looked out the front window at the storm approaching out over the lake and noticed the light shimmering through the same turn of the century imperfect glass that was throughout the Colonial Inn. The hotel was old. Maybe she'd love that, too.

Wendy reached over and touched my wrist with her fingertips. My skin came alive. "It's starting to get dark. Maybe you should light the grill."

I went outside still feeling where she had touched me and began to pour charcoal into the split rock grill that her great-great grandfather had built. During my tour of the cottage, Wendy had said that he'd been a lumber baron in Michigan's Upper Peninsula. That was why Michigan had been so important to their family even though no one lived there permanently now. I wondered what she had meant by baron, but didn't think it polite to ask. He'd probably owned four or five counties, and maybe he even had a proper houseboy like Walt's, someone who knew his guests' drinks.

Bullfrogs in search of a mate were croaking in the distant swamp. In the stillness before the storm they seemed louder than I'd ever heard them. I chuckled, remembering that years before Dad had had an option to buy those marsh lands across the road from the back of the hotel, but lacking the money and fearing that when his option expired, someone else might buy them to develop another hotel, Dad gave the option to a wealthy resorter in exchange for a promise that he'd create a nature preserve. Dad, certainly not an environmentalist, triumphed on the deal. "If I can't have the land, I'm going to fix it so no one can—just those damn frogs." Maybe, I thought, our family wasn't that different from the Johnsons, just smaller time.

When I returned to get the chateaubriand, Wendy had piled more logs onto the fire, and the old stone fireplace that stretched to the ceiling now had a roaring fire. And in its reflection the aged pine walls shadowed around us. I stood there with the front door still open, taking it all in and reminding myself how exceeding beautiful she was. But just then with a loud thud, the wind came up out of nowhere and blew the door shut, a reminder that I had to get cooking before the storm.

By the time the chateau was medium rare, (something I had learned to tell by touching the meat), a light rain had started to fall. Quickly, I brought the steak plastered with course kosher salt and freshly ground peppercorns, as well as the white asparagus and carrots that I'd grilled, into her cottage. I let the meat rest for a few minutes, carved it, then served Wendy. Not waiting for me to sit, she took at bite, then looked up at me. "Um! Incredible."

We dined, drank the Saint-Émilion I had brought, and talked about the future. Wendy ate with real enjoyment, seeming to savor every bite. She apparently liked good food; we'd have that in common, I thought. I told her of my dream to own the Inn and what it meant to me, and what I had done so far to secure it. She seemed more vivacious and charming as the minutes passed, and I became more relaxed.

She sat on an old wooden chair at the end of their long dining table, listening intently to my story of trying to acquire the hotel and, between mouthfuls of food nodded assurances. But there was something missing that I couldn't quite figure. She seemed to love to talk about ideas, like going to law school or buying the hotel, but her eyes glassed over whenever I started talking in detail about my plans.

She told me she was majoring in general studies—"a bit of everything," she said, and that she lived in a sorority house, the same one where Annie had lived when she went to Michigan.

A smile crept across my face as I remembered Annie saying that she'd seen some pretty resort girls coming out of the cottages near the hotel. She had thought that they would have ties to the area and perhaps not have the need to succeed that she and Jennifer had. Annie thought that might be perfect for me.

I wondered if Wendy could be that girl. She had said that she was eventually going to law school in New York, but that was a year away. Things could change. Next fall, she'd be in Ann Arbor, a place I knew well. Her eyes seemed to be full of fun and I thought, what the hell, let time take its course.

A lightning bolt banged through the air as if heaven itself was telling me to slow down and be careful. But I was young and impetuous—and so was she.

The next morning we awoke in front of the smoldering ashes of what had been a glorious fire. Not knowing what to say, I just looked at her. Then it happened all over again. But afterwards I still didn't know what to say. Then she broke the silence.

"Look out at the lake. It shines the morning after a storm, don't you think? Come on, let's go swimming. It's a shame that we have to put our suits on. I wish this was a deserted beach instead of a staid resort."

"I'd like to take you to a place like that."

"Maybe one day you can, or I'll take you there. But for now, just go swimming with me."

In her father's tartan plaid bathing suit that barely stayed around my waist, I raced after her toward the beach. My mind processed the twin complexities of wearing the swimsuit of a man who had been one of my biggest foes and wondering what was in his daughter's mind. I wasn't sure what she thought about what had happened. Did she really like me, or was it just a fling for a smart rich girl going places fast? But for that matter, I wasn't sure what was in my mind either. But I realized that it didn't matter for the moment. The moment was good enough.

I chased her into the frigid lake.

Coughing with cold water, I stammered, "I caught you."

"Oh, no you didn't. No one ever catches me. I only let them hold me. You understand?"

"I do. But I want to keep seeing you."

I regretted that statement immediately because I had revealed too much inside me. But she merely said, "Silly, of course you can. I'm yours for now. What do you have planned for us to do today? I like to be entertained."

"How about breakfast for starters? Let's go into town and see what's open. I'm starved."

"Sex does that to me, too. Didn't you always feel hungry the next morning after a big date back at college?"

"Yeah," I said, wondering how many such big dates she had had back at Michigan. I was wishing that maybe I had had a few more, just to be even with her.

I had planned to spend the day keeping the model open, but that could wait. I could take the day off and, for that matter, more. Why not? I was tired of working.

"After breakfast let's go kayaking. I know a river that you'd better not screw up on. Are you up for it?"

Wendy kicked toward the shore. "You know the answer to that. Now feed me."

CHAPTER 17

I'VE JUST HAD SEX WITH A COOK

A couple of hours and a couple of ham and cheese omelets later, Wendy and I were kayaking the Sturgeon River, the most challenging in lower Michigan. Since Wendy had claimed to be an expert, we decided to try the upper portion, which traversed some desolate country where no one bothered to clear dead logs from the river. This was, it turned out, a bad mistake.

A half-hour into the adventure Wendy ran her kayak onto a pile of gnarled tree trunks lining a bend in the river. Quickly the kayak rolled, began filling with the rushing water, and sank, pulling her with it. A few seconds later her head bobbed up.

"Help, my foot is caught," she called, then again went under.

I leapt from my kayak into the icy water. In the seconds it took to reach her, I thought of how this river had taken lives, one even the previous summer, and kicked myself for attempting it. The ends of the branches tore into my arms as I dove down toward her. The logs jammed deep in the black swirling water weren't going to give easily, but I kept pulling on them, trying to free her foot. After a few more seconds I was able to pull her free. She sprang up to the surface. The kayak, too, came free and, upside down like a submerged submarine, it floated down the river.

Wendy splashed about and yelled with delight as if she was taking an afternoon swim. "Don't worry about the kayaks. That was the greatest experience of my life!"

I stared across the frothy water at her. By this time we were both floating down the river behind our kayaks. I thought she was either crazy or the most vibrant woman I'd known.

"'Nothing as exhilarating as to be shot at without result,'" she yelled.

"Who said that?"

"Oh, I don't know; some famous author. But it's true. And it's a hell of a lot more fun to experience than read about."

"I'm not so sure about that. I like being alive."

"Oh, don't be silly. Swim over here and kiss me."

God, I couldn't believe it. She had almost died, we were still floating haphazardly down the river with other piles of logs waiting to snag us, and she wanted to be kissed. Oh, yes, I was going to do that. The hell with the white water, rocks, and logs; I had never met anyone like her before, and it was intoxicating.

I swam over to her. After a few kisses in the middle of the raging river, I began to forget about the frigid water, the sharp rocks scratching my legs, and the fact that our kayaks were going on without us. Wendy pointed to a small sand beach across the river.

"Let's swim over there and finish this."

"But that's in plain view."

"I'm throbbing all over from our near death experience. Do you want me now or not?"

Sometime later we swam down the icy river to discover our kayaks stuck in another pile of driftwood. And I was stuck, too; I was falling in love.

A few hours later we'd returned the kayaks to the livery and were headed home in my Mustang. Wendy sat quietly looking out the window. I was enjoying the silence and reliving the afternoon, noticing that the top buttons on her blouse were undone.

Suddenly she said, "What exactly do you do at the Inn? Everyone says your dad is still running the place."

That wasn't what I wanted to talk about, but I felt I owed her the truth. "I cook."

"Oh, that's so funny."

"Not really as funny as you think. I'm the chef and run the dining room. The maitre d' reports to me. That's how I can get you the job."

Wendy looked at me with a snarl. "My God, I've just had sex with a cook. I hope my sorority sisters don't find out. I'd never live that down."

I glanced over at her, remembering that she'd grown up spending her summers in an association that valued people by family names and wealth. But still I desperately wanted her so I attempted to explain.

"Yeah, but it isn't what you think. I make the sauces and oversee things. The cooks do most of the work. My food is known throughout Northern Michigan and even farther."

Wendy looked away from me, saying nothing. After a moment when the silence became too unnerving, I added, "I'M FAMOUS, Tim Brown, the duck cook," hoping that a bit of humor would lessen the tension.

It must have worked because she looked back at me and laughed. "You don't wear a white uniform and tall hat, do you?"

Not wanting to tell her that on special occasions I did, I said, "Most of the time I wear khaki pants and a white shirt. I keep a navy blazer hanging by the kitchen door so I can grab it when I go out into the dining room. It just looks better that way."

I looked ahead at the empty highway and wondered who I was fooling. Did the navy sports coat really make a difference? I was still a cook.

"Listen. I never planned on being a chef. Things just happened. But it's been good for me. It's given me a platform to sell my real estate and make a hell of a lot of money."

But I could tell from the look in her eyes I was losing her, so I decided to change the tone of the conversation. "Well, there's one big advantage to dating a chef; you can eat well, and I know that's your favorite thing to do."

"Second favorite. You're forgetting the beach already?"

She laughed and I let out my breath.

"Never! But let me romance you with my culinary delights this summer. It's going to be my last summer in the kitchen because next year I'll own the hotel. And you have my word that I won't show up at your sorority house next fall in a chef's uniform."

"That's awfully presumptuous."

"What, offering to work my heart out to feed you?"

"No, planning on showing up at my sorority house next fall. We've only known each other a little over a day."

"I'm sorry; I didn't mean to rush things. I only thought . . ."

"Don't. Next fall is a long way off. What are you going to feed me tonight? I already know where a chateaubriand leads."

I laughed, but felt my heart sinking. A few hours earlier I was her lover. Now I felt like her servant. "How about duckling ala orange?"

"Those little creatures are so cute. Thinking about them won't help my sex drive."

I said nothing. Her sex drive didn't need help; apparently it just needed frequent feeding.

Chapter 18

A dap of toothpaste makes the condo lived in

Over the next few weeks I helped Dad get the hotel ready to open. I was busting my butt unpacking laundry and kitchen supplies, moving TV's and beds and shuffling around everything else, just as I had done for the last seven years. There was always a lot to do because Dad didn't believe in having a big crew. "They'd just sit around," he'd say. Dad was honestly convinced that one man could do more than two. "So why waste the money?"

Even while being trapped in Dad's preseason boot camp, I still squeezed out a few hours each afternoon to sit in the model of my condominiums. No matter how much I feared upsetting Dad, I had to keep my condominiums available for sale. I lived under the misconception that at any day someone might come in off the street and buy. I had done so well that I felt I could just make the rest of the sales happen on my own. Now in the warm, restless days of June, I couldn't allow myself to worry that Mrs. Baldwin's contacts were the only way to sell my condominiums.

As the hotel's opening date in late June approached, I spent less time in the model and helping Dad and more time with Wendy. Dad didn't like it, considering all girls to be fungible.

"You have all winter, nine months, to chase all the girls you want. Isn't that enough? I kept the damn place for you."

The day before opening, Dad decided, as always, to have the front steps painted. Since his first summer, he'd put this ritual off till the last minute so that his first guests of the season, like Mrs. Baldwin, would have the privilege of walking up stairs unblemished by opening deliveries or careless employees. Dad had always worried about it raining on the day he was going to have the steps painted. With the hotel opening the next day it would have meant that the steps didn't get a fresh coat of forest green paint that year—a terrible thing to a hotel man like Dad. But with dogged determination, he put off the painting each year till the day before opening.

During the years that John had painted the stairs, he'd always told Dad not to worry; he simply wouldn't let it rain. It was like John had had some inside deal with God. Even when the sky clouded up, it had never rained on John's steps and that had been so since 1945. Just to be safe, during the last few years since John retired, he still came by when the steps were being painted just to tell Dad that it wasn't going to rain—and it never did.

On opening day at about five o'clock in the afternoon Wendy and I were sitting on the front porch just above the freshly painted steps. It had been a hot day and the long shadows falling across the high-ceilinged porch felt good. We were savoring a cup of hot tea with fresh lemon, waiting for Mrs. Baldwin to arrive. Her driver had called from Petoskey a half hour earlier saying that she would be at the hotel soon.

Wendy, fidgeting, set her cup down. "I don't have too much longer. I'm having dinner with my father tonight."

"She'll be here in a minute. I want her to meet you."

Just then Mrs. Baldwin's white Mercedes Benz station wagon pulled up in front of the hotel canopy.

I rushed down to the car, opened the passenger door, and hugged the lady who had done so much for me.

"Help me up the stairs," she ordered. "I don't want to use that damn wheelchair. And I need a drink."

When I got her up to the porch, she looked at Wendy and said, "Is this the girl?"

"I guess that's me," said Wendy.

"Oh, goodie. Get me a Stoli and let's talk."

I sent a bellman to help Mrs. Baldwin's driver settle in to his hotel room and ordered drinks for all of us.

Looking at Wendy, I said, "Mrs. Baldwin's husband was a lawyer."

I was hoping that Wendy would talk about her desire to go to law school, but instead she simply said, "That's nice."

"Well dear, what do you want to do with your life?" asked Mrs. Baldwin.

"Oh, I don't know," said Wendy glancing at her watch.

"You're being modest," I chimed in. "Tell Mrs. Baldwin that you want to go to law school."

"Come on, dear, what kind of law do you want to do?" said Mrs. Baldwin, raising her vodka to her lips.

Wendy leaned forward and said in a raised voice, "Like I said, I don't know," drawing looks from guests sitting at the other end of the porch.

Mrs. Baldwin set her drink down. "I may be old, but I can hear. You don't have to speak so loudly."

"I'm sorry, but I have to get going," said Wendy, standing and heading for the stairs.

I watched her disappear, wondering what had gone wrong. Did she see Mrs. Baldwin as a boring old lady whom she didn't want to waste any time with? Or was she concerned about being viewed as my girlfriend? Looking back, I can see that I should have followed her and asked what was wrong. But at the time, I was young and in love and didn't want to upset her. Wendy didn't do well with questions.

Mrs. Baldwin took another drink of Stoli. "I don't see anything special in that girl."

I leaned over and put my arm around her. "I'm glad you're back."

I wanted to ask if she had any new prospective buyers in mind, but after Wendy's snub, now wasn't a good time. I still hadn't sold the six remaining condominiums. I worried that all the hotel guests and neighbors who were going to buy already had.

Mrs. Baldwin finished her drink and turned to me. "Get my wheel chair. I'm tired. I'll have room service tonight."

Helping her into her wheel chair, I noticed that she appeared even frailer than the previous season. I should have asked about her health and how she was feeling, but my mind was on my own matters. Instead all I said was, "Okay."

The next morning after I finished cooking breakfast, I headed across the hotel front lawn to my model condo. I sat in the living room and looked at Annie's painting of the bridge, now hanging over the sofa, and thought about where my life was going. Annie would never have treated anybody with such disrespect as Wendy had shown Mrs. Baldwin.

A few moments later, Wendy walked in swinging her tennis racket. "Hey, it's a gorgeous day. I been up playing tennis with my father. Want to go sailing?"

"Nah, I got to spend some time in my model. I've got to make these last sales or I won't have the money to buy the hotel in the fall. I'll make it up to you later. We've got all fall, too. I'll come down to Ann Arbor and see you every weekend."

Wendy stopped swinging her racket and looked at me. "Let's worry about today. Don't you love me?"

I stood and gave her a kiss, but inside I was worried. I had fallen in love with her, but now I had to focus on making sales. My profits were locked away in the last six units. Without selling them, I wouldn't have the money to buy the hotel from Dad in the fall and he might not hold on much longer. My goal of the last eight years was in jeopardy. Surely, I thought, Wendy would understand. Wouldn't she want me to be secure, to be a hotel owner instead of a cook, particularly if we were going to be together?

I wanted to talk to her about Mrs. Baldwin, to tell her that she needed to apologize. But I was too enamored to bring it up. Instead I said, "How about I decorate one of the condominiums for us to share? I know you don't like staying with me in my little kitchen apartment."

"That'd be great. I feel like a waitress sneaking up the backstairs for a tryst with the boss. And can the dog stay up there? He's so inconvenient."

"Sure," I said, wondering about the waitress comment. She was a waitress, wasn't she?

She gave me a hug, headed out the door, then stopped. "I'm sorry if I was short with Mrs. Baldwin. Forgive me; I just get nervous when father is around."

A few days later I had the new condominium decorated. I didn't tell Wendy, but the wicker furniture came from K-Mart and the bedding from the hotel. I placed Annie's bluff picture over the fireplace, thinking that the woman who commissioned it might be pleased that it was finally going to hang over a mantel.

The afternoon I finished decorating, I showed it. Why not? With Mrs. Baldwin's health failing, I could see that she wasn't going to be able to help me much, so I needed to keep all my options open. The couple loved it, wanted it as is, saying I had an excellent decorator. They recognized the style of Annie's painting, having seen her work in Key West.

Key West, I thought. Annie did have a bohemian streak. "You can have everything but the painting," I said. "It was a gift from the artist."

"Were you close with her?" the wife asked.

I smiled. "Once."

Leaving to get the purchase agreement, I heard the husband say, "We were lucky to get his unit. It must be the best."

That quick, unexpected sale gave me the idea that any unit that I occupied would be considered special. My presence lent an air of credibility.

Furnishing three more units in the next week, I spread my clothes and some personal possessions around, making it appear that I lived in each one.

Wendy wasn't happy about moving around as the units were sold, but at that point her happiness wasn't my first priority. Nothing was going to stand in the way of my desire to own the hotel. At least I was standing up to her.

I kept the units spotless, except for a dab of toothpaste on the bathroom counter or such to show it was occupied. First I would show the professional model, just to be safe. Then I would say, "You know, I live in one of the condos. Would you like to see my unit? I love it here, great neighbors."

Sales came like magic. By late July, I only had two more units to sell.

Moving around the condos reminded me of when Dad moved us to the basement of the hotel so our cottage could be used by a tobacco convention. The hotel was sold out, so there was nowhere else for their hospitality suite. At eight years old, I thought of it as an adventure, but Mother took a different view. She came home from an afternoon of golf to find poker games and stogie smoking in her living room.

That evening when she protested, Dad began talking about President Eisenhower's world tour and how great Mamie was—his way of handling anything unpleasant; change the topic and move on, though I wonder how Mrs. Eisenhower would have handled a move to the basement.

As a little boy, and later, I couldn't believe that Dad would just bulldoze Mother into moving to the basement. But today, I appreciate their marriage of fifty-one years. Dad knew that Mother would understand why they had to move, and he knew it without even having to talk to her. Mother was a good hotel wife, always putting the business first. But over the years I've seen that a lot of people aren't willing to do that. In most small family businesses, there are those who succeed by sucking it up and paying the price, and those who complain and make excuses.

CHAPTER 19

EASY MONEY ISN'T LIKE HAVING A REAL BUSINESS

The summer of 1987 drifted along sweetly. I relished every minute. In the early mornings I watched over the culinary efforts of the cooks, making sure that the blueberries were on top of the muffins and that the hollandaise sauce for the eggs Benedict was smooth and rich.

After breakfast I'd spend a few hours in my model condominium developing prospects, which frequently led to sales. In the late afternoons when the sun hung endlessly over the bay I'd sail with Wendy. Evenings I was back at the cast-iron stoves, grease and all. But later I'd have dinner with Wendy at a candlelit table by the pool, eating entrées like rack of lamb or tenderloin Béarnaise, and spent my nights with my arms around her.

But summer was coming to an end. Harbor Springs sits north of the forty-fifth parallel, which makes it closer to the North Pole than to the Equator, and farther north than much of Canada, so summers end quickly.

By mid-August the backs of the leaves on the big maples leading down to the dock were no longer a fresh green, but more of a dried, silver color. The first hint of red was even beginning to show in a few precocious leaves. But as sweet as summer had been, I looked forward to the fall and the hotel closing as I never had. I would have it all—the hotel and the girl of my dreams.

Fall also meant football season. Michigan under Bo Schembechler was supposed to have another great team, and I'd go to Ann Arbor for every home game. Wendy and I would sample the cuisine in all the best restaurants there. Then, when the fall was over, we'd go to the Rose Bowl game and find some little inn near Pasadena that was like the Colonial Inn.

On the business side, with the hotel still open, Dad would be too uptight to talk about selling. But I desperately wanted him to at least acknowledge my success. So on a late August morning when the wind hadn't yet come up, I caught him on the front porch of the hotel, leaning back in a wicker rocker having his morning coffee. It was black and steamy, the way Dario and Benny drank it.

I sat next to him and opened a Diet Coke. "Pretty damn good summer, huh?"

He didn't answer. He just sat there looking out at the lake. I knew there wouldn't be many more days like this when the bay looked like a mill pond.

"I sold all of the condos," I announced.

Dad continued to sit there without answering, then pointed to a birch tree a few feet away. "Did you know that tree was Dario's favorite? In the final days each fall before he left, he'd sit here on the porch and stare at it."

I nodded. I'd seen Dario sitting there many times.

"He'd never seen trees like that in the Philippines or in Florida. That's a Michigan tree. Dario always wanted to stick around in the fall and see it change color. I told him we could have martins on the porch then as good as in the summer, maybe better. But he never stayed."

Dad hesitated, then spoke without looking up. "I miss him. And Benny, too, even if he did talk too much. Thank God, I still have John, even if it's only to turn the water on and off."

Dad looked straight at me and went on, "I miss all those guys, and the guests, like the Silversteins. This hotel has been my life. I've put everything into it. Time has passed so fast, goddamn it."

Dad stopped as if he'd just thought of something, then pointed down the porch toward an extra wide chair. "It seems like just the other day that I was sitting over there planning our very first menu with Dario."

"Well, Dad, the future looks pretty good, too. I've made a lot of money."

Returning to the present as if jerked back, Dad retorted with a bark in his voice, "That's easy money, like gambling. It's not like having a real business with employees and guests for a lifetime. You've built up nothing."

Mother was right, I saw. Dad had been the main show, and now a new star was rising. He'd have a hard time adjusting.

Suddenly the porch door banged open and a desk clerk came through it, screaming, "I've called an ambulance. It's Mrs. Baldwin. She's fallen out of her chair."

Dad dropped his coffee, splashing his light-blue pants as we bolted down the front steps. We found a number of guests gathered around Mrs. Baldwin and one of them kneeling over her. In the distance I could hear a siren filling what had been the silent air.

Three days later in the early evening, Mrs. Baldwin's housekeeper called to say that the private jet sent to get her had arrived back safely in Washington, D.C. Mrs. Baldwin was stable in the intensive-care unit at George Washington Hospital. The housekeeper knew nothing more, but would keep me informed.

Later that same evening just before closing, Dad barged into the kitchen. "Get out on the back porch. We got to talk."

I turned away from the blasting heat of the broiler. "The kitchen isn't closed. I got six more orders to plate up. Can't this wait?"

"No, it can't."

I threw my apron down, wiped hot sweat and lamb grease from my forehead, and followed Dad out to the back porch by the garbage hopper, which had always been his favorite place to have a private conversation—or so he must have thought it would be private.

Swatting away horse flies that had come from the depths of the refuse, Dad said, "I've just been told that I'm incompetent. Can you imagine that? Over fifty years in this business and I'm subjected to that kind of humiliation. And it's your fault."

"My fault? Goddamn it. I've been in the hot, greasy kitchen cooking. Are there complaints on my food? What the hell did I do this time?"

"Plenty, I could have sold out years ago and avoided this crap if it weren't for you."

"Oh, that again. What happened now?"

"These waitresses are poorly trained. They're the worst I've ever seen. I just fired the maitre d'. He was worthless. You hired a real jerk this year. Your real estate and your new girlfriend are all you care about. She's ruining you!"

"You fired the maitre d'?" I stammered.

"Yeah, the girls said he never showed them a damn thing."

"And you took their word without even talking to me?"

"That's right. It's my hotel."

I swatted a fly off the back of my neck.

"We had another party of four walk out of the dining room because no one bothered to come to their table for an hour! And they're hotel guests. They let me have it!"

"Damn it, Dad. The last time that happened, a waitress had just forgotten her table assignments. It wasn't the maitre d's fault. He can't watch every table. Don't you remember? I got the waitress to apologize to the guests."

"Well, there'll be no apology this time. These guests are checking out it the morning. The girls say that you've really screwed up."

"I'll work things out with the maitre d'."

"Don't bother. He's in his room packing."

Then Dad was gone, leaving me alone in the darkness.

An hour later on the moonless night, Wendy and I were dangling our feet in the cold water at the end of the hotel dock. I had taken her down there to cool off from both the hot still night and Dad's temper. I figured that an ice-chilled bottle of Chardonnay and some reassuring conversation would restore my sanity and recharge my self-worth.

"That was totally uncalled for. Awful. Why don't you just leave?" said Wendy.

I sat there silent, looking out at the water.

"I was standing by the porch door when you followed your Dad out there like a puppy. I'm ruining you? I wouldn't take crap. Do you want me to go tell him off?" She drank her wine. "Goddamn it. Stand up to him! Is the damn hotel worth it?"

Good question. Maybe it wasn't worth it, I thought, and for a moment considered quitting. Maybe she was right—Dad could take the hotel and shove it. Then I looked up and saw the lights shimmering far across the bay in Petoskey. But I saw I had come too far to let one incident change my life. Dad must have known that this would be his last summer and was having a hard time letting go.

Wendy went on, "The waitresses are totally taking advantage of the rift between you and your father."

I wondered what I had done to turn the waitresses against me. Then it came to me, as obvious as it was. It was Wendy whom they hated. She got the best schedule, only working dinners, never getting up for breakfast. And because the guests knew that she was my girlfriend, she got the best tips.

Maybe Dad was right after all. Maybe Wendy was ruining me.

CHAPTER 20

SQUIRRELS FEAST FROM A BROKEN HEART

A week later, on the last day of August, Mrs. Baldwin's housekeeper called at noon to say that she had regained consciousness. With her prognosis slightly better, she'd been moved out of intensive care and would be undergoing a number of tests that afternoon, but I might be able to call her in the evening. She gave me the phone number.

I promised myself that I would call Mrs. Baldwin that night and tell her that I had closed on the last of my condominiums and that it was just a matter of waiting till the end of the season to buy the hotel. Hell, that wasn't what I needed to say, I realized. I needed to tell her how much I appreciated what she had done for me.

The last two weeks had been hell with Dad's constant bitching that I was spending too much time on the condos and Wendy. But my inner self kept saying that my patience would be rewarded.

After lunch, exhausted and still concerned about Mrs. Baldwin, I went down to the dock to relax and think. As I stretched out on the warm planks and stared at the whitecaps on the bay, I heard Wendy yelling from her porch.

"Hey. Take me sailing. It looks just like it did when we first went out in your boat."

"It's a bit rougher, actually."

"Oh, come on. You're the guy who almost drowned me kayaking. You can't be afraid of a little wind."

A few moments later Wendy and I had swum out to the boat, unhooked her from the mooring, and were hoisting the sails. I stared at Wendy in her wet bathing suit next to the bobbing mainsail as the boom banged back and forth in the shifting air and forgot about Dad and Mrs. Baldwin. Wendy was gorgeous, and I wanted her even more than on our first sail. Except for having told me to stand up to Dad, she hadn't said nor done anything to indicate that her feelings for me had weakened. But I was still worried that the tension of the last weeks had damaged our relationship.

"Now I can take it easy," I said. "We'll spend a lot more afternoons sailing and can go out to dinner. I want the last weeks of the summer to be perfect."

I knew I had the condominium money in the bank, so I figured that I didn't have to worry so much about Dad. My second cook had learned well and could finish the season as the chef. But I still felt apprehensive about my plans for Wendy and me, remembering that Dad thought it a mortal sin to leave the dining room and go somewhere else for dinner. But I wanted to make my relationship with Wendy more normal, and going out seemed like it would help.

I went on, "I'm even going to give the old boat a good waxing. Maybe I can bring back some of her original red color. I'm tired of sailing a pink boat."

Staring at me as if distracted, Wendy answered, "I'm glad you're going to have some time off. You've been so wound up."

Just then the wind caught the sails, heeling the boat over and throwing Wendy up against me. She gave me a quick kiss, straightened herself up on the cockpit bench, and went on, "Now I want to say some things. They're important. I adore the color pink, and I'll always remember this old boat. I don't need any dates in restaurants after the unbelievable summer. We've dined at the pool, the dock, and the beach with unbelievable food."

I looked at her, thinking that I'd found the perfect girl.

The afternoon went by in a blur, the boat pitching with the chop of the waves as we tacked back and forth across the bay, unaware of anything but each other. All too quickly we were back at the mooring and swimming to shore. But the water wasn't ice cold as it had been in May. Likewise, the newness of our relationship was gone, but replaced, I hoped, by something warmer and lasting.

Back on the dock she asked, "Can you get us a cup of hot tea? I just want to sit on the end of this dock a little longer and take in every last bit of this afternoon."

I looked at her long, wet hair and smiled. "Of course."

She touched my hand. "It's been simply too prefect to end just yet; please do it. I want to be here by myself and think over something."

A few minutes later I returned with a pot of tea, fresh mint, a little lemon, and two cups on a silver tray. I poured the tea, portioned the mint, squeezed the lemon, and waited. We sat there on the bench at the end of the dock with only the waves breaking the silence.

Finally Wendy whispered, "I'm leaving tomorrow."

"What? I thought you had three weeks left before school."

"I do, but something has come up. My boyfriend is coming back to Ann Arbor earlier than I thought. It's best that I just tell you straight out, don't you think? I couldn't tell you on the boat; the afternoon was just too perfect. I didn't want to ruin our memories."

Shocked, I stared at her. Then I gazed out at the Rebel on its mooring. I wondered how such an old sailboat had lasted so long. Would the next storm, like the one we'd had that night back in May, strip her from her mooring and dash her to pieces on the rocks hidden in the water just before the beach?

Wendy asked, "Well, don't you have anything to say?"

"I honestly don't know what to say. I'm stunned."

I'd been blindsided. Even with the turmoil of the last couple of weeks, Wendy and I'd been inseparable all summer. Her words seemed inconceivable. I didn't know how to react. Mustering all my strength to hide my hurt, I said, "Let's go to work."

We left, not holding hands nor looking at each other. As we came up the beach she turned toward her cottage and I moved toward the hotel. There were still ducks to cook.

She called, "I'll be a few minutes late. Be a dear and tell the maitre d'." Then she added, "Can we have a farewell dinner?"

I stopped and turned toward her. I wanted to tell her to go to hell. One last dinner? But I had to have some answers. Had I been completely used?

"Yeah, we can have dinner. Some fresh lobsters came in today. Would that make more memories for you?"

"Don't be sarcastic. Maybe dinner tonight isn't a good idea."

Realizing that I had nothing to lose, I moved toward her and asked, "Why didn't you tell me about the boyfriend back in May? We could have been together all summer anyway."

"Would it really have been the same? We were true to each other for the summer, and that's enough, isn't it? If you knew I had a boyfriend, it would have been just the same as those older local women you've been with."

"They were only in their late twenties."

"Well, I'm only twenty, and that seems old to me."

Wendy had reached the front steps to her cottage where she turned toward me, her damp blonde hair blowing in the wind.

"But even at thirty-five you don't seem old," she said. "But there are other things."

"What other things?"

"Let's talk tonight. This isn't going anywhere now."

A second later she was gone as her front door swung shut.

The evening passed without me leaving the kitchen. Previously I had been cruising the dining room every half hour to accept compliments and introduce Wendy to the guests as my girlfriend, making her tips explode.

That night, however, picturing her tip money going toward a nice bottle of red wine for the boyfriend in some cozy little bar in Ann Arbor, I didn't feel any desire to go into the dining room.

When dinner was over I hoisted two large lobsters from a pot of boiling water and arranged them on a tray with vegetables and tiny potatoes. I winked at Wendy, which was our usual signal that our dinner was ready and began walking, this time without waiting for her, out of the kitchen toward the pool, where a busboy had already set a table with polished silver, a brass candlestick, and red straw flowers. Wendy, who was clearing the last of her dirty dishes, went to change, then followed me.

I sat at the table by the pool and opened a bottle of Saint-Émilion, the same Bordeaux that we'd had on our first dinner. I could barely hold back my tears and wondered what the hell I was doing. But I had wined and dined her all summer; why not tonight?

Acting as if nothing had happened, Wendy appeared in her red sundress, as bubbly as ever.

"The lobsters look great. I'm so hungry."

I sat there, making no effort to stand and pull the chair out for her as I had done all summer. Instead I noted twilight was about to end and it was happening earlier than it had a scant few weeks before.

Her casual, superficial air made me about ready to call off the evening. But she bent over and kissed me long and hard. Then she looked up, saw the bottle of wine, and broke into tears. Again, not knowing how to react, I simply watched. After some minutes she stopped sniffling, sat down, and started to crack one of the claws.

In the soft darkness settling around us, I wondered why she was crying. She was the one dumping me, or perhaps I thought she had realized that she had made a mistake, the kind that she would regret for years.

"Can't we talk?" I said, looking straight at her with a faint smile.

"No," she whispered, "the evening is too special. Let's not ruin it."

I knew her, and that meant that her decision was final.

Thinking of another unhappy fall with me alone in Harbor Springs and Wendy having sex with her boyfriend after football games was too much.

I exploded. "Enough memory making. I don't care if the lobsters get cold, I want some answers. What other things were you talking about this afternoon?"

"Do you really want to know? Isn't it enough to say I have a boyfriend and I'm leaving tomorrow?"

"No."

Slowly laying down her fork, she said, "Alright then, his name is Tom. He's a third-year law student at Michigan this fall. He's from Annapolis and grew up sailing. He's been at Woods Hole this summer doing marine biology research. I met him in March this year and we were in love instantly. I didn't know anything about sailboats until I met him, and, of course you've taught me a lot this summer."

"Go on!" I raged, thinking that all the sailing lessons I'd given her were for someone else's benefit. Even all the discussions we'd had about law school were probably so that she could get closer to him.

"Well, Tom is going to be a corporate lawyer, probably on Wall Street. We'll have so much fun just being together, in New York. I'll be in law school there."

"So this was a done deal before we met."

With an unsteady voice she said, "You wanted to know more. Well, now you have it."

I sat there, not saying a word. Wendy shifted from side to side on her chair and looked toward me, and then away. Tears began to stream down her sunburned cheeks.

"I love you. I'm just not in love with you. I never could have been because I was already in love with Tom. There wasn't room for you."

Wendy told me that I was a great guy. She knew that I would be a big success. I'd probably own a bunch of hotels one day. She invited me to come see her in the fall when I came down for football games. She would fix me up with her sorority sisters. She couldn't bear the thought of not seeing me again.

"Maybe if I had met you first, things would be different," she cried.

"So after our first date you planned on just continuing a fling all summer?"

"I don't have it all clear in my own mind. Things just happened."

I was trying to hold my anger back, but failing, I said, "You're a self-serving bitch. You do things just like your father—screw anybody if it serves you."

Wendy straightened her back and let her eyes bore into me. Apparently, things hadn't gone as neatly as she'd planned—I wasn't going to just slither away and accept her excuses. "You asked for it, and I'll tell you. You're nothing but an overrated cook and a flunky for your Dad. You've made some money, but look at how you've lived to get it. No girl, including me, would want to put up with all that crap between you and your father. I've never seen people fight so much. I'm glad I am leaving. I tried to make this ending sweet, but you wouldn't accept it."

I stood. "When I'm being stabbed in the back, I don't need things sweet. They can be just as rotten as Hell. You just wanted to ease your conscience."

"That's just it, all the fighting. Is it worth it? You're never going to get the hotel."

"What?" I said, wondering how I could have been in love with her.

"No, you don't get it. Your dad will never sell the hotel to you while he's alive. A person like him can never quit."

I kicked the chair behind me over onto the cement. "You'll see. I'll buy the hotel this fall."

Wendy went on telling me that it was never going to happen. I was nothing but a glorified gopher, a lackey to do my father's bidding. She never thought of me as the manager of the hotel. "You're pathetic," she screamed, rushing up from the table and grabbing her purse.

"I'll accept that I'm nothing but crap, but I have one other question."

"Go ahead. Let's get it all out."

I looked up at the sky. The stars appeared to be on fire, burning and whirling about. Maybe, I thought, the boyfriend had been just an excuse to get rid of me. "Do you really have a boyfriend, or did you just make him up?"

"You'll never know."

And with that she left, running across the hotel grounds and out of my life.

I righted my chair, sat, and stared at the two dead lobsters on the tray, looking at each other as if forlorn.

Sometime later, the bottle of wine empty, I found my way back to my condominium and fell asleep in my bed under Anne's painting, oblivious to Teddy Bear's snoring on the floor next to me. Later that night, the birds, chipmunks, and squirrels would feast beyond their dreams on lobster, leaving a mess for the yardman in the morning.

CHAPTER 21

CRACKED PLASTER, A LOSS AND GOOD ADVICE

After breakfast I sat in the chef's office, which was only separated from the main kitchen by a chicken wire wall, so I could hear the commotion of pots and pans banging and the dishwasher humming. The combination of the noise and the befuddlement in my mind from my blowup with Wendy made it hard to figure how many lamb chops to order.

It was now eleven o'clock. Wendy would be nearing Ann Arbor and the arms of her boyfriend, if there was one. I still wasn't sure. Nothing about her or the summer made sense. But she was painfully right about one thing; I had been a flunky for my father. I began to doubt that he would ever sell me the hotel.

Through the yellowed, grease-covered windows in the back of the room I could see over the kitchen parking lot to the tops of the big maple trees in back of Wendy's cottage. They were waving back and forth in a stiff breeze. Today was the beginning of the fall winds and not a time for sailing. I worried about my little Rebel on its mooring. It would have to be taking a beating. Soon I'd have to pull her out for the winter.

A new chill in the air also hinted that summer was ending. It was, after all, the first day of September, and the cottage owners and hotel guests would soon be returning to exciting big cities like Chicago. I had money now and could seek my future elsewhere, but where would I go?

The shrill ring of the old black phone on my desk shook me.

"It's Mrs. Baldwin," said a low, husky, almost unidentifiable voice.

"My God, how are you?" I blurted, ashamed for having forgotten to call her the previous night.

"Did your last closing go okay? You got the money?"

"Yes. And all is well here," I lied.

"Listen, I don't have much strength left. This hospital is Hell. Damn it. I need a Stoli. I wish you could make me one."

"So do I. I miss you. I can never thank you enough for all you've done for me. I just don't have the words."

"Don't worry about that," she said with a tired voice. "I've always known you appreciated me. Why do you think I kept helping you?"

I told her about Wendy. She wasn't surprised. She'd seen it all along. Wendy was a young girl who didn't know her own mind. I shouldn't take anything she'd said seriously. She was different from Jennifer or Annie, who had really cared for me. She said that both Wendy and I needed to grow up. I should look back at the summer as a fun time, as Wendy probably did.

Mrs. Baldwin now told me about having had too much Campari as a young college girl and waking up on the beach in Naples, Italy with a strange boy next to her. Neither had any clothes on. She didn't even know his name, but she hoped he had had a good time that night. She said that I should hope that Wendy had a good time that summer. And that was it. I should move on as Wendy had done.

As the phone went dead I stared at the bare light bulb in the cracked plaster ceiling, trying to get Wendy out of my mind. I tried to concentrate. Dad had never painted the storeroom ceiling, but damn it, I promised myself that when I owned the hotel, I'd paint it.

Ultimately I was unsuccessful at putting Wendy out of my mind and my life. Afterward it was difficult to have a meaningful relationship, I had grown so mistrustful. That was probably why I didn't marry until I was forty-eight. Through the prism of time I can see that it was silly to let her upset me and change me. I had been able to manage most everything in my life, except Dad. And I felt at the time that I was winning him over. Wendy was a cold reminder that many things in life, like the whims of a young girl and the desires of an aging father, simply can't be controlled. I would have saved a lot of pain if I had taken Mrs. Baldwin's advice. But that was hard to do.

The next morning I was again sitting at Dario's old self-made plywood desk working on my daily orders and thinking that in the thirty-six hours since I'd seen Wendy an eternity had passed. The phone rang. I reached across stacks of invoices to answer it. Mrs. Baldwin's housekeeper was on the other end. She was making the first on a long list of calls she'd be obligated to make that day. Mrs. Baldwin had slipped back into a coma, after talking with me yesterday, and had passed away quietly in her sleep around midnight. The hairs on my arms moistened as I thought I'd probably been the last person to talk with her. I sat at Dario's desk in my cubbyhole office looking out the yellowed window. So much had changed so quickly, and I felt adrift.

I stood and began walking a few slow steps toward the kitchen's back door. I ignored the creaks in the floor and thought only of dragging myself out into the sunlight before depression might bring me to my knees. I'd go to the hotel pool. That was a sun drenched place where I could open my soul to the sky and seek redemption. Redemption from what, I wasn't sure, but I needed to think; somehow I knew that would make me feel better.

I couldn't go back to the dock which had always been my special place to seek comfort. Wendy had chosen that as the place to dump me and in so doing had, probably forever, denied me its use as a sanctuary.

When I got to the pool and laid on a lounge, thankful my wobbly knees had carried me that far, my thoughts blurred and I collapsed into a fitful nap. Sometime later, and I wasn't sure how long, I awoke to find Allen lying on a lounge a few feet away. When he said hello, I told him about Mrs. Baldwin.

"I'm so sorry," he said and I knew he meant it because I could see dampness forming in his eyes. "She was a great friend to all of us. I'll never forget her dinner parties or the way she made me feel so welcome when I started coming back here. She was kind to my parents, too. For you it's probably like losing your best friend. God knows you were close."

I pressed my lips together and nodded, looking at Allen, relaxed and tan, catching some of the last few rays of the summer sun. I was mourning for Mrs. Baldwin, but also for my relationship with Wendy. Further, her brutal but frank parting words made me realize that Dad would likely never sell me the hotel. I felt like hell about all of it, and I guess it showed.

"You look like you're in a trance."

I shrugged.

"There's no one here, Tim. You can talk about it if you want."

I looked up at the big oak next to the gate of the pool. "Maybe that would help. It's not only Mrs. Baldwin. It's Wendy, Dad, the hotel . . ."

Allen patiently listened as I spun out my tale of woe.

"My God, you've got the troubles of Job. I can't help you with Mrs. Baldwin. You'll have to grieve for her by yourself. Have a couple martins for her tonight. That's what she would want you to do."

"As always."

Allen smiled. "Good, You're lightening up. Did Mrs. Baldwin say anything about Wendy?"

"Not really," I prevaricated.

"You're thirty-five, she's, what, twenty-one, maybe?"

"Yes."

Allen sat there for a moment frowning, looking up at the cloudless blue sky. "That's the problem—she hasn't lived life. There's no way she could understand what you're trying to do. Mrs. Baldwin, John, and I have watched you struggle since you quit your job in Chicago to pursue your dream of owning the hotel. A young girl like Wendy may have five or six different dreams by the time she's your age. The whole world is in front of her. If something isn't working out for her, she has time to do something else."

I saw Allen was right. Wendy, with her youth and naiveté, would have had trouble understanding my ambitions.

He went on, "From what I've heard, all Wendy did this summer was whine about your father and the hotel. You're lucky to be rid of her."

"Ah, you've summed it up nicely," I said with an ironic smile.

"You'll just have to forget her—I'll bet that's what Mrs. Baldwin told you. Wendy isn't wasting any of her time getting over you, so why should you waste your time on her?" He pulled a couple of Heinekens from a cooler by his side and handed me one. "Now, on to your real problem, your father. That's what you should be thinking about. You've got a damn good thing going here. Don't blow it. I know something about your situation, having grown up with a similar dad."

"Yes, I know. You had it hard," I said, thinking of Dad's story about Allen ruining his father's business. Herman Silverstein must have blamed a lot of his misfortunes on Allen, then told the unfortunate story to Dad.

"I did have it rough, but that's why I can help you," said Allen. "We had a lot of bickering, like you and your dad, about how to run the flower shops. As a result, nothing got done, and our financial troubles only worsened. When my dad died, the flower shops had to be sold for next to nothing. My biggest regret is that I never confronted my father, man to man, like you should do before it's too late. Give him a business proposal, and tell him why you want to buy the hotel. He's getting tired. Those lines in his forehead weren't so deep a few years ago, and he doesn't bound across the grounds like he used to."

Allen set down his Heineken and looked me in the eye. "You want to know the biggest tragedy? That son-of-a-bitch died leaving me with self-doubt. I had such low esteem that I've never made it past selling clothes. I didn't think I had it in me to do anything else. That's why it was so long before I could get the nerve to come back to the hotel. Even then I had to make up that ridiculous story about being a pharmaceutical representative. I've been living a lie the last seven summers because of my God damned old man."

I reached over and grabbed Allen's arm. "I'm so sorry. You know I've never told anyone your story and never will."

"Thanks, did you know that Mrs. Baldwin knew?"

"No."

"One night last summer in the cocktail lounge a guy was joking about the fellow in town who had sold him a suit. He made the salesman sound like an idiot, and my self-doubt came raging back. It must have shown on my face because Mrs. Baldwin powered her chair up to me and we started talking. She had a way of drawing things out of you, and it wasn't long before I had told her my story."

Allen picked up his beer and wiped his eye—I couldn't be sure whether it was sweat or a tear. "I'm fine now, really. I've had years to live with my situation. It's too late to help me, but maybe I can help you reach your goal. Perhaps there's a reason our families are connected."

"Don't get too heavy on me, Allen. I've had a lot of emotion the last couple of days," I said, trying to lighten up the conversation.

"Don't worry, from here on out, it's just business advice. In fact, that was my problem. I didn't see it as a business situation; it was just too close and personal. You've got to cool down, take a deep breath, and relax. Now is not the time to talk to your dad. Just continue being the faithful son and servant for the rest of the summer. Your dad is like an old lion facing his last summer. Don't aggravate him, and be humble. Your time is the fall after the Inn closes and his anxieties subside. Then confront him, man-to-man in a non-emotional business discussion. Prepare mentally for it as you would any business deal, like selling your condominiums. I think he's waiting for the right way to be asked to sell to you. Remember, it's his decision to say yes or no."

I nodded. "I guess that makes sense."

"Prepare a written purchase agreement and a business proposal showing how you'd keep the hotel successful. There's something more than money out there. The Colonial Inn is more than a hotel to your father; it's the culmination of his life's work. He's loved it for years. He's not like other hotel owners who only want people to check in, check out, and pay the bill. Most of them act like they're running some kind of factory. For your Dad, it's always been about service and relationships. He didn't sell to the developer, did he? If he didn't want you to have the hotel, he would have sold it by now."

Allen stopped talking; I knew he was waiting for me to absorb this. I wouldn't be able to just nod my head so I took a deep breath and looked him straight. "I'm starting to get it."

"Good, then keep following me. I think—and this is big—he wants you to have the hotel, but he wants to know that you're going keep it going for the long haul. Can you convince him?"

I signed as if a big weight had been lifted from my shoulders. Allen had opened the door for me to see that it was still possible to complete my dream of owning the hotel. I stared at him, feeling both relief and caution. "I think I can."

"Another thing," urged Allen, leaning back in his lounge, "if I'm not cutting too deep here. You shouldn't have bragged to him so much about your real estate profits. I've heard him say that your money was made through luck, and that it wasn't the same as profits from a lifetime in a business."

"You're right. Every time I talked about my condominium profits, he was turned off."

"Well, you're learning. Now, the most important thing is for you to prepare to be turned down. You have the rest of the summer to think it over. You aren't going to do anything until fall, right? If he doesn't want to sell you the hotel, then that's it. You won't be a failure because you'll have your pride and his respect. If that happens, be a man, take your money, and go elsewhere. There are other hotels. But I don't think you'll fail!"

Chapter 22

Moose burgers in Canada

As fall approached with the inevitable closing of the hotel, each day my nerves became more unglued. As jittery as a graduating college student realizing real life was about to come down hard, I wondered if I really had the guts to confront Dad and if this might be my last summer at the hotel. Allen phoned every few days telling me to hang in there, but I didn't know if I could.

It was now two weeks after Labor Day, when the dining room closed, but Dad was still renting rooms out. Seeing him alone sitting at the front desk one morning, I lingered.

"Dad, have you decided when we're closing?"

Deciding when to close was a game that Dad played every year with the employees. He didn't want the help making plans to leave, wanting to keep his options open.

"Every year I tell you the same thing. There's no point in committing too early," he said. He struck a match to light up a Camel, took a couple of long drags, and looked at me. "You remember the year I announced that we were closing Labor Day and suddenly a big telephone company convention booked for a week later? Most of our staff had already made plans, so we ended up with a full house and no help. What a disaster."

"Dad, that was twenty years ago. We got the convention only because the hotel they were supposed to stay at had a broken water main. You think that's going to happen again?"

"Maybe not, but what's it cost to wait? We're making a few dollars every day, the weather's still warm, and guests are still coming. Is there some special reason you want to know? You seem anxious to close. You have some special plans with that girlfriend of yours down in Ann Arbor?"

I hadn't told Dad about Wendy dumping me. With the hotel on the line, I had tried to be upbeat in whatever I told him.

"No, nothing special, Dad. Wendy and I are through."

"No loss there. She was in it for the money. I could smell that from day one. Girls from wealthy families are nothing but problems. Dated one myself back at the University of Miami. There was no substance to her. She never would have made a good hotel man's wife and neither would Wendy. You're lucky to have her gone. You'll pick up some local gal for the winter, go skiing, and have a great time, not so demanding. You always do.

"You've got the world by the tail. I wish I could be young and single like you. I wouldn't get married till I was maybe sixty," continued Dad, putting his big burly arm around me.

A buzzer went off and the yellow light on the hotel switchboard flashed, signifying an incoming call. Dad bent down behind the counter and picked up the desk phone.

"Good morning, Colonial Inn."

As Dad listened I saw his shoulders sag. He pressed the phone to his ear. "I see. That's horrible. I'm so sorry," said Dad, groping for his still-smoldering cigarette. "Can I do anything for you?"

I waited for him to hang up the phone, clutching the edge of the counter. Finally he set down the receiver and said, "They found John dead this morning in his cabin. He must have been there a couple of days."

Dad collapsed into a chair behind the desk. "Goddamn it. Now who's going to drain the hotel?"

I thought about the days when John was waiting for me after school in the hotel station wagon and how he stood there in his khaki uniform, as Dad had instructed him, just to the side of the front door so that the Colonial Inn lettering could be seen. I'd wondered why that had mattered at Central Elementary School, but to Dad, decorum always counted.

"The kids at school will know Colonial Inn is a fancy place," he had said. "There's no telling—someday they might send us business."

As I looked at Dad in the chair behind the front desk, puffing on another cigarette and gazing out the lobby window, I realized how distant those days were and, for Dad, how much had changed.

Finally Dad made his decision to close the hotel. After it was shuttered and I'd finished crawling through the dust to drain the pipes, I took Dad on a fishing trip up to the bush country of northern Ontario. I wanted to take him to a place where we could talk man-to-man and I could present my plan without distractions.

I'd rented a log-and-tarpaper cabin, where the loose fit floor planks on the porch moved up and down as we rocked back and forth in our chairs. The scent of pine mixed with that of fall. The evening's quiet was broken by the calls of another guest returning from the lake, yelling that he'd caught the biggest trout of the season.

Not yet night, I could hear distant timber wolves baying in the stillness of the desolate bush, their cries echoing against the barren granite cliffs. I was glad to be within the confines of the camp, with a circle of light and warmth from logs burning in a fire ring before us, and in Dad's aura. I still felt, as I had when I was a little boy, that if the devil jumped out of the dark woods, Dad could handle him.

I opened a couple of Molsons, handed one to Dad and took a gulp of the other. "Dad, you've done a lot of work with the hotel over the years. Just keeping it going with all the repairs was a job in itself."

I had spent weeks preparing my speech, but now faltered. It didn't help that a few weeks earlier when I'd tried to talk to him about the hotel, he'd shut me down cold. I hoped he'd listen now.

Gazing at the October moon rising over the lake, I thought back to my weekly "business lunches" with Dad when I was a boy. Remembering how we discussed things over chicken à la king, even though I was then but a child, I found sudden courage, and the words came.

"I want to buy the hotel. But if you don't want to sell, I'll understand. I've got a plan all written out. You want to see it?"

Remembering Allen's words that the hotel meant more than mere money to Dad, I stopped short of saying that I could give him cash, more than the developer. Instead I spoke from the heart. "I'm grateful you didn't sell eight years ago. I've had a chance to learn a lot."

Dad set his beer down on the rustic table and looked out into the darkness. I knew he had to be wrestling with the biggest decision of his life. He knew that I had the money and must have known that I'd be asking to buy the hotel. Eight years earlier, he'd been willing to sell, but now he had even more time invested.

I wondered if he'd come closer to trusting me with his life's work. Three days ago I had grabbed John's big pipe wrenches and told Dad that I was going to drain the hotel. A smile crept over his face, reminiscent of the one he had when I rode a bike without training wheels for the first time.

Now that I'm closer to his age and look back on this scene, I understand that Dad was also facing his own mortality. Eight years earlier, when the offer from the developer was on the table, Dad joked that he wasn't dying or going out to pasture. He was going to get a pile of money and play golf. But during the ensuing years, the realities of advancing age had set in. Dad was closer to dying. Maybe now he thought that selling the hotel would push him closer to the grave.

Dad, his face creased in thought, leaned back in his rocker, lit a Camel, and said, "What's your plan?"

I leaned toward him. "I've been listening to some of our newer guests. They say that the hotel is getting tired and needs a renovation. We're not keeping up with the competition. Our rooms still have studio couches that have to be made up at night into twin beds. No one under fifty can fathom this, and we have to explain to would-be guests that our cool lake breezes make air conditioning unnecessary. The era of old long-term guests, who accept the hotel the way it is, is coming to an end."

I held my breath for a second and thought of Mrs. Baldwin, whose passing did represent a game change. Even though she no longer stayed in the hotel, she had many friends who did, and they wouldn't be coming anymore. The beds were probably just fine for them, and I was sure that at their advanced age they didn't care about air conditioning. There weren't going to be any more widows like her. That was for certain.

I didn't want to press too hard, but I still continued. "The two and three-day guests want beautiful rooms with modern conveniences and amenities. They don't care about our dining room. They want to try other places and see the area."

Dad began slowly rocking and puffing on his cigarette. I saw I was getting through.

"The dining room and bar are a lot of work, and they lose money. Few hotel guests dine or drink with us anymore. We've become a club for the cottage owners, the very folks who opposed our condominiums. Our dining room is only a quarter full on the week nights, then bulges over on the weekends when the resorters don't want to wait in line with the tourists at the town's restaurants."

The resorters who for the most part demanded impeccable food and service were in my opinion unprofitable gourmets who should be standing in line with the masses.

"Dad, like it or not, the business has changed. The days of playing the gracious host while providing lavish service are gone. It just costs too much and we can't increase the rates enough to cover the real costs of gourmet dining. I want to stop the losses by closing the dining room, then put the savings into renovating hotel rooms."

I looked over at Dad, but there was no immediate response. I became aware his eyes were intently fixed upon my face. It wasn't a mean stare, just a deep reflective one. Then his lips pursed. "It's hard to believe that you, the great chef, would suggest that."

I wanted to suggest that we look at last year's income statement, but didn't. I felt that I was making my point anyway and didn't want to hurt Dad's feelings, so I simply answered, "It's the only way."

Dad appeared to still be studying me. "How about breakfast?"

"I'll set up a breakfast bar: fresh fruit, toast, cereals, and blueberry muffins, the way Benny made them with blueberries oozing out of their tops."

Dad went on, his eyebrows pinched a bit. "I've already booked a large wedding for the end of June next year. They're going to fill the whole hotel. You'll have to still do it."

Dad was talking as if he'd already agreed to sell me the hotel, but he hadn't said "yes" yet. The breeze coming in off the water chilled the night air. I'd laid out my plan. It wouldn't do to press him for an answer. Now I had to wait for him to make the next move.

Finally Dad turned to me and said, "How much?"

I had him. Dad had always said that, in a business deal, the first one to mention money is the loser.

"Two hundred thousand more than the developer was going to give you eight years ago, all cash."

"Done."

I stood to shake his hand. But as he stood he threw his arms around me. His whiskers scraped my cheeks the same as they did when I had been a little boy and he'd catch me when I jumped off the dock.

We opened a couple more beers and walked down to the lake. We stood there for a minute, then he laid his big arm on my back. "I'm proud of you."

Later that night, I paddled a canoe out onto the dark lake. I snuggled down into its bottom with a wool blanket and gazed up at brilliant stars. I had won. I got the hotel. But I got something more; Dad's respect. I realized that's what I had been after all along. Looking back, I could see that what really concerned me wasn't failure or success, but how Dad might perceive me.

My journey hadn't been without cost. Back home, another long winter lay ahead with only my dog Teddy Bear for company. I had no girlfriend nor, for that matter, friends, except Allen, but he didn't live in Harbor Springs. I'd been so busy pursuing my goal that friends hadn't seemed important. Thinking back, I realize that there's a cost to success. Some pay it and some don't. I did.

CHAPTER 23

FATHER'S DAY WILL NEVER BE THE SAME

Michigan didn't have a good football season the fall of 1987, going six-and-five and ending up in a lesser bowl game in San Diego. But it didn't matter to me. I didn't have a beautiful girl to take to the Rose Bowl and never found out if there was a little hotel like the Colonial Inn in Pasadena. Instead, I spent New Year's Eve at a Chinese restaurant near Harbor Springs, devouring egg rolls and their version of pressed duck. Earlier I had loved the winters in Northern Michigan, but now they were starting to wear on me.

My previous condominium venture had been so successful that I thought as long as I was stuck alone another winter remodeling the hotel, I might as well roll the dice again. I reasoned that a six-unit motel building in the middle of the hotel grounds wasn't not a good use of land and thought that if I tore it down, I could build an even larger twelve-unit condominium and make even more money. I didn't have the money to complete the building, but figured that I'd just finish the outside, landscape it, and use my old trick of nailing sheets over the windows to hide the unfinished inside.

That part of construction wasn't expensive, so there wouldn't be a lot of risk. And now I was a seasoned developer, or so I thought, with an existing project as a track record. Surely now, pre-selling an unfinished project near my existing one wouldn't be difficult, even without Mrs. Baldwin.

I skied a lot and watched over the workmen at the hotel and condominium, and somehow the winter passed. But each day dragged into the next and I savored nothing, not like when I was snuggling with Wendy and selling my condominiums the past summer. But in the end the result seemed worth it. The old hotel looked great and the new condominium looked promising.

On a warm night in early May when the croaking of bullfrogs shook the windless night air and not a leaf had yet appeared on any tree, I sat on the front porch of the hotel waiting for Mother and Dad. I had the lights blazing, the canopy up, and two martins mixed. I wasn't reflecting on the past like I had been on that frozen night in December when I returned from Chicago eight years earlier. Dad would be here in a few minutes to inspect my hotel.

Dad and Mother pulled up in front in their new Lincoln, as if they were checking in. I rushed down the stairs, hugged them and handed Dad a martin. "Let's go see the hotel."

I wondered what they would think about my renovations. Inside, I hurried down the halls flicking lights on. I showed them the changes, one after another, hardwood floors, fireplaces, white wainscoting capped with chair-rails, and granite bath-counters.

"Amazing," said Dad, looking at Mother, who nodded approval.

I went on for some time pointing out improvements like I was a building contractor.

Finally Dad said, "Enough. The rooms are gorgeous. I wish I could have had rooms like these."

I cracked a smile. That was the best compliment he could have given me, one hotel man to another. Dad always said that the most important comments, the ones you really pay attention to, come from others in your industry.

He went on, "These rooms are worth a lot more than I was charging. You'll need somebody who knows how to sell them."

"Yeah, I'm worried about that."

Dad looked at Mother and said nothing. She nodded and placed her hand on his arm, then he looked back at me. I wondered what he was thinking. I was young, just thirty-four, and excited about all the renovations and the upcoming season. He was old and his business was gone. He would have nothing to do but play golf. That apparently wasn't enough for the old lion.

He cleared his throat. "How about me? I'd like to stay on. Help you sell these rooms."

Here was the man who had conceived me, molded me, protected me, ruled over me like a dictator, the one man in the world I most loved and feared, on whom I had depended, asking me for a job, to do my bidding, to be under my rule.

I remembered that warm summer morning when Dad was standing in the blue water off the hotel dock with his gray-haired chest, looking like Poseidon. He wanted me to jump, but I stood there looking down at the rocks on the floor of the lake. The ripples on the surface seemed to make them bounce around. I was thinking I could never do it, that the dock was too high. But Dad said, "You've got nothing to worry about as long as your old Dad is here."

I closed my eyes and leaped, expecting to hit the icy cold water. But instead Dad's big warm arms snatched me out of the air. In that instant, surrounded by Little Traverse Bay and its green hills, I knew that the world would be a secure and welcoming place as long as he was there.

Looking back, I might wonder what had happened to alter that relationship in the years through law school, my time in Chicago, and working for him at the hotel. I had turned to Dario for security to comfort me when I left for college and for Chicago, not Dad. My childhood had been secure, almost idyllic. But when I'd gotten older, my relationship with Dad changed. He expected more and demanded a toughness that wasn't yet in me.

But now I see that my relationship with Dad hadn't changed as much as I had thought. He'd been there all along, guiding me; I just didn't see it. He was trying to toughen me and season me in the only way he knew, to succeed in a world fraught with insecurity. I see that, if he had just welcomed me back from Chicago with open arms, sold me the hotel on an installment sale, or, worse, let me inherit it, I wouldn't be the man I am today

Maybe now that I had proven myself, Dad could work for me. With the hotel gone from his control, he was now the one without security. Now I needed to catch him, as if he was leaping into my arms.

"Your mother and I have been talking. Retirement isn't for me. I don't want to manage anything, just help in sales."

I wondered how long Dad had spent thinking this out. He'd be helping at the hotel, but he wouldn't be in direct competition with me. It was brilliant. Dad and I would be a team, and I was proud that he would be part of my fulfilled dream. I shook his hand.

"It's a deal."

June 19, 1988 began as a still Sunday morning with a cloudless sky and a still lake. The hotel hadn't opened yet, and it was a lazy and relaxed Father's Day. But tomorrow all hands would be on deck. The grand opening and big wedding were only five days away. And so was my first season as a full-fledged hotel man.

Sitting on the hotel front porch waiting for a meeting with the bride and groom, I sipped a Diet Coke. A big yellow bumble bee was flying just below the railing, its buzzing the only sound breaking the stillness. The soon-to-be-wed couple had telephoned the previous day, wanting to reduce their drink prices. I was furious. I'd officially closed the dining room, but had agreed to still cook their damn duck. But my renovations had cost a lot of money. I was ready to give in, as I didn't want them moving the wedding elsewhere.

However, that previous night Dad told me, "Stand your ground. It'd be too embarrassing for them to change locations."

A blue Mustang arrived with its top down, and bride and groom, looking a bit sweaty, like they had just come from the tennis court, got out. They were both wearing white shirts with little alligator logos. How cute. I chuckled, thinking back to the after-the-alligator party that I had attended with Annie years before.

Slowly I ambled down the stairs to greet them, trying to appear as nonchalant as possible. "What a beautiful day. Hope it's just like this for your wedding."

Wanting them to realize how special the hotel was, I pointed to the green and white floral cushions on the porch wicker and said, "Mother had them redone for Sonny Hemingway's book signing. Everyone was here."

Dad had told me to call their bluff and make it seem like canceling wouldn't be a big deal, so I went on quickly, without giving them a chance to talk. "I can only offer you a Coke. I don't have anything else."

I then added that this was because I hadn't ordered anything for their party yet, implying, but not actually saying that cancelling wouldn't cost me anything.

"No, thank you," said the groom, glancing at his bride. He coughed and cleared his throat. "We're here just to get some business over."

"That's too bad. Our porch is such a beautiful spot."

Remembering that Dad had told me it's best to appear relaxed while making your opponent uncomfortable, I plopped down on a chaise lounge without making any gesture for them to sit. I pointed out the rows of freshly planted red geraniums lining the porch.

"I don't know any other place in all of Northern Michigan like this. Think of your guests pulling up here next Saturday."

"That's not the issue. We've found another place that will give us cheaper drink prices. We'll have to move the wedding, and the hotel guests, too," said the groom, glancing back and forth at his bride.

Knowing that he was waiting for me to give in, I took my time. "We've had a deal since last September. You knew our policy."

"Yes, but we've just now figured up how much this is going to cost."

"That's too bad. If you want to take the wedding elsewhere, that's okay. But your guests' room deposits are non-refundable."

"Can't we work this out? We don't want to move the wedding if we don't have to," said the bride, pushing her long blonde hair from her eyes.

"No. It costs lots of money to keep the hotel going."

Watching her fuss with her hair, I wondered if she really cared about the liquor price. I figured that maybe the groom put her up to it. It was probably his chance to play the big shot to her father.

Dad had said that kind of thing happens many times with the summer people. Someone from a lesser station in life marries into an old family. He then feels that it's incumbent upon him to step up to the plate, make himself appear worthy.

The first time this opportunity presents itself is usually the wedding arrangements where the under-classed groom can show both assertiveness and financial acumen by vigorously attempting to chisel the hotel. The prices of accommodations, food, and liquor are always way in excess of what they should be, or so he informs his prospective father-in-law. Dad had had this game practiced on him many times and wasn't going to go along, and neither would I, so I just sat there continuing to sip my Diet Coke.

I thought about Wendy and how truly lucky I had been not to have been taken into her family. I would never have been able to be the unworthy son-in-law and spent a life sucking up to Dick Johnson.

There were a few more seconds of the bride glancing back and forth between me and the groom, then she said. "All right, leave it alone."

Apparently she'd had enough. They nodded at me and left, never having had a chance to enjoy the porch. Too bad; it was such a glorious morning. Dad was right, they'd given in.

Propping my feet up on an ottoman, I surveyed my grounds and savored my Diet Coke as if it were Courvoisier. In the tranquility of that warm June morning I thought about how much I still needed Dad. I was the hotel owner, but I still didn't know it all. I had needed Dad to tell me to hang tough with these people. I wondered if I could ever be the man he was. Would I ever be able to just know the right thing to do?

He'd always been there to advise me. I remembered back when there was a summer theater near Harbor Springs, staging Broadway traveling productions. Many of the actors stayed at the hotel, and they'd give us free tickets.

When I was eight I saw a show there about a beautiful girl falling in love with a Canadian Mountie. In the end she sang a love song and threw a red rose out into the audience. I'd wanted to catch that rose so badly that I dragged Annie, my summer girl, to that show every night for a week. Before the final show Dad had said, "You got to ask for the rose. Stand up before she throws it." I did, and the actress threw the rose right into my outstretched hands.

Thinking back, I realize that the hotel was my rose. I'd asked for it, held out my hands, and grasped it. Dad had taught me that I had to ask for things, work for things, and grab them when they came my way.

Dad had been right about the bride and groom, as he'd been so many times in my life. Even though he was now working for me, he was still my father, still the soul of the hotel.

A few moments later Allen Silverstein pulled up in front of the hotel in his old Cadillac. I had told him that he could check in early. He sat on the porch railing across from me as he'd done at so many of Dad's cocktail parties.

"How's the new owner?"

"Great," I told him and went on about how excited I was about the season and having Dad's help on the desk.

"I'm glad the two of you are going to work together. It wasn't always that way at the hotel."

I leaned back and sniffed the sweetness of the freshly planted flowers as Allen continued.

"My grandparents stayed at the hotel in the 1920's. The widow Eaton owned it then, and her son, like you, did everything from cooking to maintenance. You're lucky. When Mrs. Eaton died, he didn't get the hotel."

"I'm glad that didn't happen to me. I owe you."

"No you don't. But you do owe your dad. He allowed you to earn your own success."

I stood and put my arm over Allen's shoulder. "I'll see you for cocktails tonight. Hopefully Dad will join us, even though he's been feeling tired."

I walked across the grounds toward Mother and Dad's cottage, thinking how much Dad had done for me. He'd sent me to college and law school, but didn't kick my ass when I quit the Chicago law firm after all he'd invested. He was hard on me when I came home, but he did let me do it. He put off his retirement so I could pursue my dream. And he did allow me the space and opportunity to remodel my old houses, build my bluff homes, and develop the hotel condominiums.

I wanted him to know that. I thought about how much I had grown in the past year, how much I had changed since that day I met Wendy. Then I had thought that money was what I had wanted. Now I knew that it was Dad's approval. A year ago, I wasn't really on top of the world; I was just telling myself that I was. I had money then, but I didn't have Dad's respect. That was yet to be earned. No one ever stays on top, anyway. There's always something, I'd come to learn, to knock you down. After everything I'd been through, I wondered what could take me down. I had a chilling thought. What would I do when I didn't have Dad?

Reaching the cottage, I found Mother sitting on her porch sipping coffee. A blue jay cawed in the distance. "Hi, Mom. Is Dad out playing golf?"

"No, his old station wagon is behind the house. I'll go upstairs. See if he's napping."

A moment later the terrible scream came, one that I'll never forget. Her disembodied words, reverberating down the stairs, blasted the morning stillness. I couldn't quite make them out, though it sounded like she was saying, "He's dead!" But that couldn't be.

I rushed up the stairs past Mother, who was clutching the top banister as tears poured down her face. "Get someone. Call an ambulance."

Entering their bedroom, I saw Dad's motionless body lying on the faded blue carpet. A circle of dried blood surrounded a wicked gash on his forehead. His mouth and eyes were wide open. The man who could have wrestled God only yesterday looked like a fallen toy soldier. It couldn't be true. I couldn't believe it. This kind of thing happens to other people, not me.

My thoughts racing, I looked around and saw that his dresser drawer was ajar and reasoned that he'd probably fallen against it when his heart gave out. I dropped to my knees, telling myself that he couldn't be dead. Maybe he was in coma or knocked unconscious. I bent over and pressed my mouth to his. His lips were cold, but I still blew hard for what seemed an eternity. I kept blowing, until finally Mother put her hand on my shoulder.

"Stop."

I stood and looked down at him. This had to be a despicable dream. It couldn't be true.

Mother hugged me and said, "No one ever had a better father."

I put my arms around her, stared at Dad, and nodded. And now, as I write these words, I'm still nodding.

A few minutes later, a dark-blue-uniformed state trooper arrived. He examined Dad, picked up his portable radio, and said, "Tell the ambulance to slow up and turn off the siren."

That night my widowed mother and I talked on the porch of her cottage. She sat on the sofa with a glass of wine as I reclined on Dad's wicker lounge chair with a martin. Fireflies flitted through the scent of lilac, much as they had on a night like this twenty-five years earlier, when Dad got up from this lounge and ordered a Saint Bernard dog for me. As I sipped my drink, part of me kept looking around for him to appear, announcing that a puppy was on its way.

I wondered if Dad had waited to die until he saw that I was safe and his life's work was in good hands. The timing was so important. If he'd died just eight months earlier, how different my life would have been. I was grateful to have achieved his respect and scared about how I was going to go on without him. I felt an emptiness that I had never thought possible and doubted that time would ever heal it. Now that Dad and I finally respected each other and could work together, he was gone. I looked over at the hotel and thought, what a team we could have made.

Chapter 24

Sunsets on the deck

On warm summer evenings I still go down to the dock with a martin, olives and a twist of lemon, and watch the sun sinking over the western edge of the lake. I look up at the green hills surrounding Little Traverse Bay and think that Dad isn't far away. Maybe he, Mother, Dario, and Mrs. Baldwin are also having a martin. And Dad would be saying in his big booming voice that he knew all along that I was meant to be a hotelman.

DUCKLING AL'A ORANGE

A RECIPE

The problem with duck and the reason most people don't cook it at home is because it's full of fat, hence a lot of grease. But this can be conquered and you will have a truly epicurean dish.

- Remove all the loose fat from the cavity, the neck, and the base of the tail.
- Next prick the skin at half inch intervals to allow the marinate to ingratiate the meat and to help the inner fat to escape during cooking.
- Then cover the duck with a thick paste of orange concentrate and allow it to sit in the refrigerator for several hours.
- Just before cooking, rub the skin with kosher salt, coarse freshly ground black pepper and the juice of a fresh orange combined with a teaspoon of Grand Marnier.
- Place the duck upside-down on a rack in a roasting pan so the bottom fat slowly flavors its way through the meat.
- After an hour of 325 degrees, drain off the fat drippings, add some orange concentrate in the bottom of the pan and turn the duck right-side-up. Keep it on the rack so it is out of the fat and cover it with a loose tinfoil tent so it can breathe.
- Slow-roast it at 350 degrees for two to three more hours while frequently basting it with drippings and orange juice. In final minutes the duck needs to be liberally doused with Grand Marnier and the skin crisped under a full-blast oven. Watch it carefully during this process so as not to burn it. The skin on a well-cooked duck is deliciously intoxicating.

I apologize for not being precise with the cooking times. All ovens are different. You'll have to experiment. Dario, my mentor was far from an exact man, and he usually drank while he was cooking so his methods were not always the same. His advice: "put plenty of booze on the duck, use the good stuff—Grand Marnier—not the cheap stuff like Dad wanted him to use and cook zee hell out of it." When you have achieved perfection, the duck skin should be dark brown and the meat a rich brown color, not pink. Don't be worried if the skin has a few burnt spots. It won't affect the meat. This is not *Nuevo Cuisine*. The sauce is simply made by heating orange concentrate with Grand Marnier. Don't cut up orange peels and add them to the sauce as a lot of fancy cookbooks suggest. Every time I have done this, even when I boiled them first, they ruined the sauce by making it bitter. It is best to keep things simple.

Finally if you want little excitement pour an ounce of 151 proof Bacardi rum on the duck just before serving and light it on fire. This won't affect the taste, but will impress your dinner guests.

About Tim Scott Brown

It seems I was born—and then I was in the hotel business. Whether I wanted to make a life in it or for that matter even liked it, wasn't a question I had time to ask until I began writing my story. I was going to be in the hotel business and still am with hotels in the Florida Keys and Northern Michigan.

My first business meeting with Dad happened at 1 AM, July 22, 1952, when I'd just arrived in this world. He was all business so it was easy to believe Mother when she said he sat in the rocking chair by her hospital bed and told me about his hotel. He almost didn't make it to that meeting—alive. An hour earlier François, the second cook, and Mac, the baker, had an argument over a woman's favors, which resulted in a meat cleaver flying through the air. A few inches different in its trajectory and I wouldn't have had a father—a life I can't imagine.

I've run elevators, called BINGO games, washed dishes, roasted Chateau Briands and fixed leaky pipes. And above all, I'm the duck chef. I have a few other achievements although they're of less importance. When I was a freshman at The University of Michigan, my creative writing professor said my work had promise. For a few weeks, I thought there might be something in life other than the hotel business.

"A ridiculous notion," Dad told me, after hearing me tell Sonny Hemingway I wanted to become a writer like her brother. So I finished college and went on to graduate and law schools, but it didn't change anything. I was a hotelman.

Then, the cruel trick happened—it seemed Dad didn't want me to follow in his steps. A lot happened and a lot was missed. (That's my story.) My mother went to her grave believing I'd never have children. Then at forty-eight, I married Tricia and we have two boys, Timmy, thirteen, who is the volunteer bellhop at the Colonial Inn and Teddy, eleven, who helps in the Colonial Inn office. It's my hope they will both become hotel men and follow in their grandfather's footsteps.

About eight years ago, Manon Graf, my surrogate mother, and long time manger of The Kingsail, one of my Florida hotels, said to me in her French accent, "Why don't you build a little office overlooking the ocean and spend a winter writing it all down?" So I did—but it wasn't just a

winter and it wasn't just an office by the ocean. It was six years, an attic
office in Michigan and lots of professional help from authors in Key West,
who made me realize that if I wanted people to buy my book, I'd
have to "spill my guts," something that didn't come easy. But it's been
worth it—I've come to know my father, who's been dead twenty-six years,
a lot better. Men in his generation, who suffered through the Depression,
served in World War II and built their businesses from scratch, kept their
feelings to themselves.

Tim and Teddy